THE CHILDREN'S HOSPITAL TEMPLE STREET

THE POST-CENTENARY YEARS (1972–2002)

BLACKWATER PRESS

Editor

Antoinette Walker

Design & Layout

Paula Byrne

Cover Design

Melanie Gradtke

CONTENTS

ACKNOWLEDGEMENTS

The Sisters of Charity and The Children's Hospital acknowledge the advice, assistance and direction of the many members of the Board of Management who gave their time voluntarily through the years. With gratitude we remember: the Hon. Mr Justice T.A. Finlay, chairman, Mrs J. Andrews, Mr F. Colthurst, Mr J. Blake Dillon, Mr G. Hendron, Mr J. Lenihan, Prof K.B. Nowlan, Mr R. Bourke, Mr A. Lord, Mr J. O'Driscoll, and Mr Justice G. Clarke. The new members invited to replace those who retired were: Mrs J. Mehigan, Mr W. Earley, Mr D. Condon, Ms M. Finlay Geoghegan and Ms M. O'Connor. Mr J. Nugent took over the role of chairman in 1985. Mr B. Strahan and Mr S. Sheehan joined the Board in 1987 and 1989, respectively. Mr Justice R. Johnson became chairman of the Board in 1993. In 1995 Ms J. O'Connor and Mr F. MacCumhaill became members.

The Hospital owes a great debt of gratitude to the chairman and the members who gave an unstinted service and remained until the Board was dissolved in December 2001.

The production of this updated history of The Children's Hospital provides us with an opportunity to say thank you to all those people who give of their services willingly to the hospital – the politicians, public servants, including An Garda Síochána, the Ambulance Service, the Fire Brigade, and all of the donors and Friends of The Children's Hospital.

In compiling this updated history, we are very grateful to the Mission Committee who over the past two years focussed on the gathering of materials. They include: Mr Martin Brophy, Sr Ann Forrest, Ms Valerie Grimes, Dr Peter Keenan, Sr M. Magdalen McPartlan, Ms Margaret Myres, Mr Ray O'Ceallaigh, Ms Anne O'Connor and Ms Alison Wallace.

Above all, our thanks to our staff who give a dedicated and committed service and make The Children's Hospital a safe and caring place.

FOREWORD

This story of The Children's Hospital had its origins when members of a small Mission Committee decided in 2000 that it would be timely to record the work of the Sisters of Charity from the time of their taking over the Hospital in 1876.

The Children's Hospital is one of the few remaining Catholic voluntary hospitals in Dublin and as such will continue under the trusteeship of the Sisters of Mercy. Indeed Mary Aikenhead, foundress of the Religious Sisters of Charity, and Catherine McAuley, foundress of the Sisters of Mercy, shared the same zeal and love for the poor and disadvantaged.

As each member of the staff of the Hospital will receive a copy of this book, it is hoped that the dedication and commitment of so many past and present members will be a challenge to all who will have the task of maintaining the ethos and spirit, which has been part of the tradition of The Children's Hospital.

Sr M. Magdalen McPartlan, RSC
November 2002

THE HISTORY

1872

A NEW ERA BEGINS...

Now these kind hearts may rejoice, and prepare to make good their works, by giving help to a noble undertaking. A good genius has been at work unsuspected in our city, and another Brobdingnagian mansion, like that so pleasantly described by Mr Hood, has already risen, like Aladdin's palace, amongst us, and is this moment standing in Buckingham-street, in Dublin, looking out, with bright, new-painted windows, across fields, trees, and cottages, away to the blue sea and the smiling hill of Howth. Our good genius has provided us with this house, decorated it with perfect taste, made it cheerful and attractive in all its appointments, and is now putting up beds in the reception of a number of lucky little inmates, as yet unchosen from countless hosts of suffering babes.

Opening of St Joseph's Infirmary for Children at No. 9 Upper Buckingham Street, Dublin on 11 November 1872, from *The Children's Hospital, Temple Street, Dublin Centenary (1872–1972).*

PRE-CENTENARY YEARS

COINS IN THE COAL CELLAR

BARRY KENNERK
RAY O'CEALLAIGH
PROF NIALL O'BRIEN

Most of us – if we have ever been in a house over 100 years old – are probably familiar with the sight of a foot scraper on the top step. These small metal implements hark back to a Victorian Dublin that was noisome, dirty and overcrowded. Usually, before entering a house, citizens needed to wipe from their shoes an accumulation of the horse manure, sewage and slops that littered the streets. It was into this environment that St Joseph's Infirmary for Children opened its doors in Buckingham Street in November 1872. The timing was apt; coming shortly after the last parliamentary session in which a proposed Infant Life Protection Bill was debated, and during which a call had been made for amendments to the Public Health Bill. The Sanitary Association had also opened its doors on Dame Street in the same year.

The Infirmary was founded by a charitable group of people led by Mrs Ellen Woodcock. It was a forerunner to Temple Street and was typical in a city that according to historian Prof Mary Daly in *Dublin, the Deposed Capital* (1984) was 'dominated by a mass of small hospitals established to cater for various religious and charitable groups'. There was clearly a strong need, however, for a hospital that catered exclusively for children. Although many of the general hospitals had wards that accepted children, they were unable to deal effectively with their needs, and paediatrics was yet to be established as a separate discipline.

There were some institutions such as the Lucan Spa Asylum that dealt with children, but these were only available to 'lunatic patients of the middle classes', according to the

Irish Medical Directory of the time. In addition, those who ran charitable institutions did so at their own expense, or depended on contributions. By 1876, the annual figures for attendances at Buckingham Street rose dramatically. This shows that the hospital was providing an important service in the area, but because it had outgrown the ability of those who had family commitments to govern it, it was handed over to the Sisters of Charity.

Temple Street during the early part of the 20th century.

The nuns suited the task of running a hospital very well because of their long history in medical care. They had been heavily involved, for example, in the 1832 outbreak of Asiatic cholera during which the penitentiary in Grangegorman was converted into a temporary hospital. Catherine Rynne in *Mother Mary Aikenhead (1787–1858)* tells us that '50-60 patients died every night' and that 'sometimes the dead-lists which were pinned to the hospital gates…included the names of all the poor women employed to attend the sick'. The nuns also took an active role in visiting the poor in their homes, and in the winter brought them food and coal from their convent on Lower Gardiner Street.

The lease on the house in Buckingham Street expired in 1879 and a new location was chosen at No. 15 Upper Temple Street. The house that the Sisters moved into had been the family home of the Earl of Bellamont and was just one among many vacated buildings in the area. The North Inner City was increasingly becoming a slum area, partly because of the general movement of the higher classes towards the developing suburbs. Falling house prices were a deterrent to builders, and elsewhere there had been a slow demolition of large tenement blocks in favour of smaller housing developments. The two exceptions to this general rule were the Mountjoy and Rotunda wards. In the Rotunda ward (which encompassed the area around Temple Street), the population was rising in excess of available housing. Mary Daly in *Dublin, the Deposed Capital* also notes that 'hospitals and similar facilities and…the decision of Dublin Corporation to site their cattle market in this area' furthered its decline.

When the Sisters entered the Hospital in April 1879 they were forced to make some changes to the building before it could be opened to patients. One of the first alterations was the conversion of the old stables into a dispensary or outpatients department. Evidence for a lean-to off the stables can still be seen in the remains of lead flashing and in some of the postholes for the roof trusses. The Sisters slept and lived over the stables (in what is now the Wages Department) and dined in the old harness rooms. The coach house was large enough to facilitate a laundry, and reception rooms within the house itself were turned over to wards. The Hospital was ready to open on 17 June 1879.

The name of the Hospital changed to The Children's Hospital, Temple Street but it was still under the patronage of St Joseph. It subsequently was advertised in the *Irish Medical Directory* for the first time in 1880. It had twenty-one beds and was staffed by the same physicians who had been at Buckingham Street, most of whom held other hospital posts. John Francis McVeagh, for example, was also a doctor at 'St Mary's Asylum and Government Female Reformatory' in Drumcondra. Thomas More Madden from London was a gynaecologist to the Mater Hospital and credited as the inventor of the long and short midwifery forceps. When Buckingham Street opened, he had just returned from service with the French army in the Franco–Prussian War. Men such as these were at the forefront of the development of paediatrics prior to the 20th century.

It is a remarkable fact that in a city where one-third of total deaths were among children under five, the death rate in Temple Street when it opened was under four per cent. To complicate problems further, there was an economic depression in 1880. This put increased pressure on the family unit, and the amount of children deserted by one or more parents rose. At that time, Dublin had fourteen dispensary officers and another set of doctors was attached to the city hospitals. They carried a huge burden in caring for the poor, and attendance at the Temple Street dispensary had almost doubled by 1885. In the same year, Madden convinced the Royal Commission (also known as the Spenser Commission) that the Hospital was vital for Dublin. It was providing a valuable service to a class that previously had been largely forgotten about. Perhaps more importantly, he argued that the diseases of children required special training.

Nursing sisters and patients on St Agnes' Ward during the early part of the 20th century.

Certainly throughout the 1880s, the medical profession struggled to become more organised. The Spenser Commission reported in 1885 that there was a surplus of hospitals in Dublin and tried to get some of them to amalgamate. Perhaps it was this call in favour of merging hospitals that Madden was so outspoken against, as it would marginalise Temple Street's position as an emerging paediatric hospital. He also fought his corner in terms of a need to address the illnesses of the tenement population. One factor on his side was that the city had a very favourable patient–doctor ratio (fourteen beds to each physician). By comparison, Liverpool had twice the population of Dublin and only four hospitals.

The Spenser Commission also believed that the poor law red ticket was being abused and that the lower middle classes in Dublin had a far poorer medical service as a result – the poor received their care *gratis* while the middle classes had to pay for it. There is a noticeable parallel here today!

Ray O'Ceallaigh provides an account of the Spenser Commission's Report on Dublin Hospitals from 24 November 1885.

DUBLIN HOSPITALS' COMMISSION REPORT

Dr Thomas More Madden is first to be interviewed. He is an unpaid physician at the Hospital. He is allowed to make a statement to the Commission. In his statement he states that he has been attached to the Hospital since its foundation in 1872 in a house in Buckingham Street. It was supported by private benevolences and the hard work of a Mrs Woodlock, well known for her support of Catholic charities in the city.

Dr More Madden: "In 1876 the management was transferred to the Sisters of Charity. In 1879 the Hospital was transferred to a commodious building in Upper Temple Street, purchased at a cost of £2,500. In the last year, the adjoining house was purchased and £8,000 was spent on the purchase and fitting up of the building. Presently there are about 80 beds available but funds only allow for the use of 36 beds. The cost of maintaining a bed in the hospital is £19.19.6d."

The staff of the hospital consists of two physicians – Dr More Madden and Dr McVeagh; Dr Maypother, consulting surgeon, and two surgeons, Dr Baxter and Dr McCullogh. Mr Christopher H. Callanan is acting clinical clerk. These are all unpaid except for the apothecary, Mr

O'Leary. Three Sisters of Charity are constantly in the wards, assisted by ward maids and a night nurse. The expenditure for the year 1884/85 was £4,528, and income was £3,046, leaving a debt of £1,482. Paying patients' contribution was £5.10.6d.

The conditions for entry to the Hospital are sickness and poverty. Protestant and non-Catholic children are freely admitted. Dr More Madden ends his submission by trusting that the Commission will recommend the Hospital's participation in any grant from public funds in aid of Dublin hospitals.

Dr More Madden agrees with the Commission that Dublin is amply supplied with hospital accommodation and that Temple Street is only a short distance from the Mater Hospital, but he makes the point that no general hospital supplies sufficient accommodation for the special diseases of this institution.

Sir Richard Martin enquires about the large garden at the back containing over an acre of ground. Dr More Madden explains that this is one of the reasons why the expenses of the institution are so small. It supplies vegetables for the house. The fowl are kept there and these provide eggs. The large air space around the Hospital is considered beneficial for sick children.

Sir Richard suggests that looking at it from a moral point of view, a child is exposed to a great risk of contamination from the sights it witnesses in the treatment of adult patients. Dr More Madden answers yes, undoubtedly. Mr Holmes of the Commission then suggests that it would be more convenient for medical students if a ward was set aside in a large hospital, to which Dr More Madden agrees, but points out that some students now attend St Joseph's Hospital [Temple Street].

Mr Holmes: "St Joseph's is practically a sort of out ward attached to the Mater?"

Dr More Madden points out that they are under separate management and that it would be difficult to prevent children mixing with adults in a general hospital.

Surgeon J. McCullogh is next to be examined. In his submission, he says that of the 284 cases treated in the wards in the last year, there were twenty-two deaths – fifteen boys and seven girls. Of those twenty-two deaths, eleven were from tubercular meningitis. He is at pains to point out that, frequently, children are only brought there when they are dying in order to get a death certificate for the burial societies. He suggests that most of it is due to pure neglect on the part of the parents. There are sixteen surgical beds and twenty medical beds in the Hospital.

Surgeon McCullogh says there is a lamentable ignorance of children's diseases and that medical licensing bodies should make a short course in children's diseases a necessity. He points out that nurses need to be specially trained in the care of children to watch for the symptoms of prostration, and all that needs to be carefully watched and noted. Those who make a specialty of children's diseases recognise in their very appearance when something is wrong.

Surgeon McCullogh gives his testimony in favour of a large children's hospital as an absolute necessity. He and the Superioress have identified a site at the back of the Hospital where a separate infectious wing might be built. He regards scarlatina as a very serious and fatal disease of children. The Hospital is at the top of a hill where there is a plentiful supply of pure fresh air. He has impressed upon the chairman that parents object to sending their children to the large hospitals.

* * * * * *

In the years following the Commission's Report, there was an attempt to establish a system of intercourse between charities in the city. To achieve this, a central office, the Association of Charities Office was set up at 45 Molesworth Street, Dublin. The office would record information regarding people seeking relief from societies. In this regard, it is important not to view Temple Street Hospital in isolation, but as a part of a whole system of Dublin charities, many which also dealt exclusively with children. They included, for example, the 'Police-Aided Children's Clothing Society', the 'Church of Ireland Clergy Widows and Orphans Society' and the Sisters of Charity School in Gardiner Street, where poor children could get their breakfast free every morning.

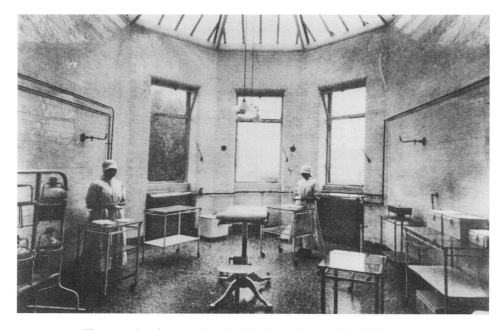

The operating theatre as it existed in the early part of the 20th century.

Books that listed charities were important to Temple Street because the Hospital could advertise for donations in them. The advertisement in *Dublin Charities*, for example, states that 'contributions will be received by any of the medical officers...or by Mrs C. Hodgens at the hospital.'

Such voluntary aid was essential because the period just prior to the 20th century was one in which the State had little or no intervention in most hospitals. The expenditure of Temple Street in 1899, for example, was £2,566. Subscriptions and donations and a Corporation grant met £1,220 of this sum and other grants made up most of the rest. A paltry £90 came from patients during the year because the poor got free admission at the discretion of the managers.

It should also be pointed out that the Hospital could not have existed in its early years, were it were not for the support of such people as Mr Bianconi – the famous stagecoach maker – and various other notaries of Dublin society. Indeed Oscar Wilde contributed on one occasion.

One interesting story told to me serves to illustrate the Hospital's early dependence on voluntary aid. Some years ago, a porter named Michael Fielding was given the job of clearing out some of the old coal cellars at the front of the Hospital. After shovelling away a quantity of coal, he discovered some old wine bottles and a number of coins. Apparently, the reason for the coins being there was that many years earlier the Sisters had placed a box in the railings with a chute into the cellars for the receipt of donations. Eventually, when the Hospital no longer had to depend solely on voluntary funding, the box was removed, but the chute remained. It is a testament to the loyalty shown by the people of Dublin to the Hospital that for a long time afterwards people continued to put loose change down the chute as they passed by. Of course, once the practice was officially discontinued, nobody came to collect the money and it lay there like buried treasure.

Hospital garden at the rear of Temple Street in the 1960s.

Except for the Corporation grant that I have already mentioned, Temple Street was not catered for by the State and in 1894 the Hospital was nearly £2000 in debt. A fête was held in the Rotunda Rooms and Garden to raise money. From this, the Moy-Mell Children's Guild was initiated and continued for some years. Its most distinguished members included Princess Beatrice's two children, who visited the Hospital during Queen Victoria's visit in April 1990.

DISEASES IN THE 19TH CENTURY

The various illnesses that children living in the 19th century might have been afflicted with is a source of great interest. Many of those presenting at Temple Street appear to have been treated for tuberculosis (TB) or tuberculosis-related illnesses; a harsh result of the appalling conditions in which people lived. The houses on nearby Hardwicke Street and Gardiner Street contained families of ten or more in one room and ailments such as arthritis and hip disease were prevalent. Some six hundred and fifty children attended the dispensary in 1884 with scrofula, which Newman Dorland describes as 'TB of the lymphatic glands and sometimes of the bones and joints surface' in the *American Illustrated Medical Dictionary*. It was essentially a disease of early life.

Interestingly, the 1901 National Census provides details on the seventy inpatients that were resident in the hospital on the night of 30 April. At first glance, the amount of children suffering from TB is striking. In some cases, the disease affected the feet and these children are described simply as 'lame'.

Koch made his discovery in 1882 that TB was an infectious disease, but it took some time for this to become widely accepted and it was not acknowledged as a significant factor in the city's high death rate until 1900. Later on in 1908, Cappagh Hospital would be set up to deal with children suffering from tubercular bone disease. When it eventually opened, treatment was 'carried out on the modern lines of fresh air, heliotherapy and splintage', according to *The Life and Work of M. Aikenhead* and many children were referred there from Temple Street.

Interestingly, up until the early years of 20th century, the turnover of inpatients at Temple Street and other hospitals was fairly low (see Table 1). Nevertheless, all hospitals in the Dublin area dealt with a similar volume of outpatients. This is indicative of a health service whose standard practices involved the retention of inpatients for longer periods of time than would be considered normal today.

Table 1. Attendances at Buckingham Street and Temple Street for the years 1874–1902.

Year	Beds	Inpatients	Outpatients
1874	18	96	1,627
1875	21	204	3,569
1876	-	184	3,323
1877	-	189	4,110
1878	-	231	2,509
1879*	-	236	3,000
1880†	-	236	3,000
1881	-	340	3,700
1882	-	240	3,200
1883	-	240	3,200
1884	-	240	3,200
1885	-	275	5,512
1886‡	40	285	5,600
1887	-	329	6,400
1888	-	329	6,400
1889§	-	329	6,400
1890	-	488	6,400
Figures after 1890 remain the same until 1894			
1894	-	500	7,080
1895	-	500	7,080
1896	-	550	6,532
1897	-	660	6,532
1898	-	660	6,532
1899	-	660	6,532
1900	-	660	6,532
1901	90	500	6,000
1902	90	500	6,000

* The addition of an apothecary and a surgeon is listed.
† Temple Street is mentioned here in the Directory for the first time.
‡ This substantial rise in patients is explained by the equipping of No. 14, purchased in 1883.
§ A clinical assistant joined the Hospital in this year.
Source: *The Medical Directory, London, Provinces, Wales, Scotland, Ireland*

Nowadays, children are more likely to be kept in hospital for a short period of a week or two and then released with subsequent outpatient referrals or dressing clinic appointments. Before this, however, the normal practice was to retain children for long intervals, even if they had injuries that were not life-threatening. Because conditions in the tenements were so appalling, patients who might otherwise have been cured often suffered a relapse when they returned home.

In the lanes adjoining the Hospital, there was a piggery and a farrier's workshop where horses were brought to be shoed. Businesses of that nature lasted in the vicinity of the Hospital up until the 1940s and 1950s, and it is from this that the 'piggery' car park gets its nickname. Although animals such as pigs probably provided a source of waste disposal for the Hospital kitchens, they also added to the filth, and since refuse was not collected regularly, it tended to accumulate in yards and streets. The theory generally held at the time was, according to Prof FOC Meenan in *Cecilia Street*, that 'hospital infection was carried by a noxious gas or miasma'. In 1865, Joseph Lister discovered that bacteria spread infection, but until his theory had become widely disseminated, the former view held.

For this reason, the usual practice in hospitals at the time was to soak bedclothes and doors with chloride of lime and Condy's Quid. It was believed that fires burning in the wards would draw up the 'miasma' through the chimney. In Temple Street, coal was delivered into bunkers under the street as it had been during the days of the Earl of Bellamont. The porters would then carry the coal up to the wards to light the fires every morning as part of their rounds, and the huge Aga in the kitchen was fuelled by it.

Waiting room in the Outpatient Department in 1914.

The X-ray Department as it existed in the early part of the 20th century.

FULLY FLEDGED HOSPITAL

Gradually, Temple Street became less of a house and more of a hospital. The central staircase inside the front door was removed and a new ceiling put into what was now the front hall. Interestingly, a statue of the Virgin Mary carrying the Infant Jesus that once stood on the landing of this old staircase today stands on the backstairs landing on the way to ICU. The marble pedestal, upon which the statue stands, features two winged cherubs, and is quite remarkable. The huge reception rooms upstairs (currently Surgical Flat and Top Flat) were dissected to make separate ward areas. This is still clearly in evidence in Surgical Flat, where the mouldings end towards the door and continue in the room across the corridor.

The family home of Charles Stewart Parnell on Temple Street also came into the possession of the Hospital in 1885 and this was fully equipped by the end of the year. In fact, the present chapel is on the site of the old billiard room of the house. The Hospital as it stands today incorporates a number of houses on the street acquired towards the end of the century. Their interior walls were broken down and corridors were joined to link them with the main building. Some original features of these houses are still extant. As one walks towards St Brigid's Ward, for example, an old dumb waiter system can be observed. This was used to take meals from the kitchen of the house up to the dining room via a pulley system. In the basement of the house (the 'dungeon'), the oval shape of wine cellars can be seen on the way towards the canteen.

It was only at the beginning of the 20th century that Temple Street began to take the shape of a modern hospital. The Operating Theatre was built in 1903 and in 1914, the new Outpatients Department was completed. This date can be seen over the doorway from the Casualty lane, as well as the Sisters of Charity motto: *Caritas Christi Urget Nos* (the love of Christ moves us).

By 1901, the little community of nuns governing the Hospital had relocated from the old coach houses to No. 14 Temple Street. There were sixteen sisters in total, including their Superioress, Christina Hodgens. Considering the drop in religious vocations today, it is a remarkable fact that the average age of each nun in 1901 was thirty-five. Two members of the community, Srs Catherine Cummins and Anne Roantree, were in their twenties.

Hand in hand with these changes came huge advances in medical knowledge. As early as 1877, H. MacNaughton in a book entitled *Clinical Teaching in Hospitals* recommended that students attending the sick should carry the following instruments at all times: stethoscope, clinical thermometer, pocket measure, scissors, forceps, probe, small scalpel, lancet, silk and silver wire, and litmus paper.

In addition to this, students were asked to carry a pocket urinary test apparatus. This is interesting, because it shows that the testing of urine for signs of illness was becoming more accepted as a standard practice. Interestingly, Victorian ideas of conduct are juxtaposed with these new techniques, however. There is a responsibility incumbent on the student, according to MacNaughton, for 'restraining youthful license and curbing ungentlemanly frivolity in the hospital ward'.

There were good prospects for young doctors after finishing medical school, and during the early years of Temple Street, graduates came from three institutions – the Royal College of Surgeons, Trinity College and The Catholic University School in Cecilia Street. The Children's Hospital had an especially close relationship with the latter, and Dr More Madden sat on the governing board of Cecilia Street after it was brought under the supervision of the Education Endowment Commission in 1891. Since 1886, medical students had to pass examinations in midwifery and surgery as well as medicine, and towards the end of the century the period spent as an undergraduate gradually increased. Although hospital positions went unpaid, it was often considered essential to obtain a post in one, particularly if a good career and reputation were to be established.

As was the case at the Mater Hospital in Eccles Street, students probably attended the Hospital during the morning to visit the Outpatients Department and the wards. Since, like most other city dispensaries, the former was only open daily from about 10 am to 11 am, the students were free in the afternoon for lectures and dissections. Money was earned after graduation from private practice, and it is notable that most of the consultants in the Hospital were also established as private practitioners.

The Children's Hospital was well equipped with medical staff in comparison to its contemporaries. County and City of Cork Hospital for Women and Children, by comparison, had a similar amount of inpatients in the period 1874–1901, yet had just one consultant surgeon and five medical officers. The Hospital in Dublin, while being well staffed with physicians, also had dental, resident and assistant surgeons. Patients were often referred there from elsewhere in the country, as the output from Dublin medical schools provided a healthy patient–doctor ratio and assured the most modern practices.

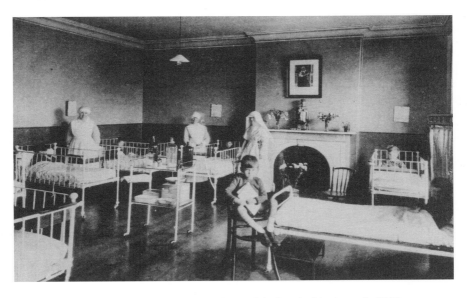

St Camillus' Ward situated at the front of the hospital in the early 1930s.

By the turn of the century, the Hospital team had expanded to include a corps of non-medical staff. Besides the gardener, Bryan Molloy, and his wife, the National Census taken in April 1901 lists the names of twelve household servants. A 'Lady Superintendent' was responsible for their welfare. The fact that all could read and write marks them apart from their working-class contemporaries and suggests that they had another role to play beyond household chores. In particular, the type of background that these ladies hailed from suggests that at least some of them were training to become nurses. Nineteen-year-old Mary Smith, for example, came from a Georgian house on St Stephen's Green. Her father is listed in *Thom's Directory* as a chemist. Mary's upbringing may have given her a life-long interest in medicine for which a career in nursing was the only outlet.

Although there were some attempts to address public health and the organisation of public hospitals during the late 1800s, it would be early in the next century before they would fully cease to be more than big houses (the two world wars were to hasten this progression). On the recommendations of the Spenser Commission, there were some hospital amalgamations in Dublin, such as that of the National Eye and Ear Hospital, which joined with St Mark's, and as a result became the Royal Victoria Eye and Ear Hospital on Adelaide Road. Temple Street was permitted to remain independent, however, having successfully created an awareness of the valuable work that it carried out.

In 1908, Lady Martin, daughter of the famous Victorian physician, Sir Dominic Corrigan, bequeathed her lands and a large house in Cappagh to the Sisters of Charity. It was decided to establish a Children's Hospital and on 8 September 1908 twelve children from Temple Street were transferred for convalescence. Cappagh remained a convalescent home for The Children's Hospital until 1920 when it was decided to establish an open-air orthopaedic hospital. Temple Street, through various fundraising events, contributed to the cost of building the orthopaedic hospital which was opened in 1924. Strong links between the two hospitals continue to the present day.

By the 1930s, the Hospital had succeeded in making the transition from a charitable infirmary to that of a modern institution with adequate equipment. Since then it has continued to add immensely to the understanding of the specific nature of childhood diseases and has helped to foster an understanding of the development of paediatrics as a separate discipline.

Convalescing al fresco *at Temple Street during the 1950s.*

During the first half of the 20th century, according to Prof Niall O'Brien, 'The Children's Hospital, similar to other hospitals in Ireland developed many subspecialties to embrace all aspects of childcare.' During the 1930s, funding from various sources, such as the Hospital Sweepstakes, gave rise to many badly needed facilities, for example, the X-ray Department, Physiotherapy Department, Milk Kitchen, Operating Theatre, and St Michael's Ward. The year 1946 saw the acquisition of St Anthony's Hospital on Herbert Avenue, Dublin 4 as a convalescent home. Great strides at Temple Street continued until the arrival of a new children's hospital in Dublin in the late 1950s, as described by Prof O'Brien:

> *Progress continued until 1957, when a new children's hospital was opened in Crumlin, Dublin 12. Some of the consultant staff at Temple Street decided that their future was at the new hospital. This had a considerable*

influence on the Hospital during the 1960s. However, at the end of that decade new blood was introduced to the consultant staff and with this a firm plan of future development was devised. At this stage, one must pay tribute to a visionary pathologist, Dr Seamus Cahalane whose foresight led to the setting up of the National Neonatal Screening Programme in 1966, and a pragmatic orthopaedic surgeon, Mr Patrick MacAuley. The Hospital owes a great deal to these men. Because of the vision of Mr McAuliffe-Curtin, ENT surgeon, a new unit called St Frances Clinic for the assessment of developmental disorders was opened in 1965.

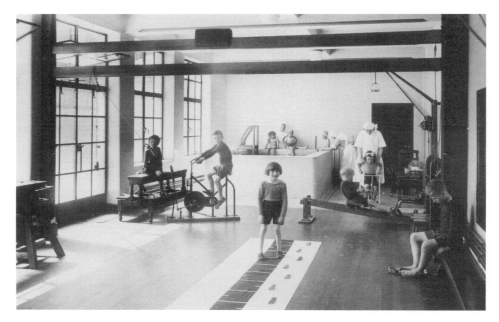

Physiotherapy at Temple Street in the 1940s.

By the time the Hospital came to celebrate its Centenary in 1972, The Children's Hospital, Temple Street was firmly established as a leading paediatric hospital in the country. The occasion was marked by great celebration, according to Prof Meenan:

The celebrations reached their climax on 11th November 1972, exactly 100 years after the opening of the 'Big House' in Buckingham Street. The

President of Ireland attended a solemn concelebrated Mass of thanksgiving in the church of St Francis Xavier, Upper Gardiner Street. The Archbishop of Dublin, Most Rev Dr Dermot Ryan was the principal concelebrant. After Mass, Mr Sean Flanagan, Minister for Lands, on behalf of the Government officially opened, and the Archbishop blessed the new nurses' home and X-ray department. Afterwards, there was a reception held in the Hospital. In the presence of the President, the Archbishop, the Minister for Lands, the Mother General of the Congregation of the Sisters of Charity, Mother Francis Rose, and a large gathering of friends and supporters of the Hospital, the Community and Staff of the Children's Hospital, Temple Street, dedicated themselves to another hundred years service to the sick children of Dublin and the country.

And so as Prof Meenan declared 'the work started by a good genius so modestly 100 years earlier had come to fruition'. It certainly had.

Mr Barry Kennerk is a former staff member of Medical Records Department, Mr Ray O'Ceallaigh is Chief Microbiologist, and Prof Niall O'Brien is a former Consultant Neonatologist at The Children's Hospital.

POST-CENTENARY YEARS

SR M. MAGDALEN McPARTLAN, RSC
PROF NIALL O'BRIEN

This history of The Children's Hospital, Temple Street is an effort to record developments and events of interest which have occurred since the original history of the Hospital was printed in 1972 on the occasion of the Centenary of the Hospital.

THE 1970s

The distinguished career of one faithful servant of Temple Street came to an end in the mid-seventies. On 30 September 1975, Mr J.P. Shanley retired as senior surgeon. In recognition of his lifelong dedication, loyalty and service to The Children's Hospital, the Sisters of Charity petitioned the Pope for a papal honour for him. The honour of the Order of St Gregory the Great was conferred at a reception held in the Hospital on 30 October 1975. Previously, in November 1972, a special dinner was held in the National Gallery of Ireland with a presentation to Mr Shanley to celebrate his Golden Jubilee of service with the Hospital.

The seventies saw the arrival of much improved services and the consolidation of links with other hospitals, as described by Prof Niall O'Brien:

> During the 1970s the general services of the hospital were improved to a new level. Further links with maternity hospitals were introduced, which augmented the management of neonatal patients requiring surgical and expert medical care. Neonatology also expanded into many other departments, notably Orthopaedic, Opthalmology, Urology, and ENT.

Radiology continued to expand, and also included a link with The National Maternity Hospital.

A number of structural improvements were also carried out during the 1970s. Building of the Clinical Laboratories commenced in January 1976. The cost of the building was £80,000. Of that amount, £50,000 was provided by the Variety Club of Ireland and the balance raised by the efforts of the Social Committee and the Sisters of Charity. The new laboratories were opened and blessed by Dr Ryan, Archbishop of Dublin on 11 February 1977. There was a distinguished gathering at this function, including members of the Variety Club of Ireland. Indeed, Mr Rick Bourke and his wife, Ivy, were indefatigable workers in the raising of the monies given by the Variety.

In 1977, the Hospital acquired St Anthony's Lane from Dublin Corporation (between Nos. 13–14 Temple Street). The Corporation agreed to open a lane on the site of No. 8 Temple Street, given in exchange. A subway was therefore built under the area of No. 8 connecting Nos. 7–9 for hospital use. The transaction of the laneway and subway cost £35,000, which was funded by the Sisters of Charity. Arrangements were made to have gates erected at Temple Street and Nerney's Court to indicate clearly that this site had become the property of the Sisters of Charity.

Contract forms were signed for the building of new theatres in September 1978. Effectively, this was phase one in the redevelopment of the Hospital. Plans for the overall development of the Hospital were next lodged with the Department of Health in May 1979. On 16 July 1979, the then Minister for Health, Mr Charles Haughey, TD, inaugurated the screening programme for hypothyroidism. Also in 1979, the 'Property at Nerney's Court' (large stores and garage) was purchased for the sum of £25,000 – and the amount paid by the Sisters of Charity.

One of the most key events of the 1970s was the decision to establish a Board of Management. In 1977 the Superior General of the Sisters of Charity appointed a Board for the Hospital. The Hon Mr Justice T.A. Finlay graciously accepted the role of chairman. The members of the first Board were Mrs Joyce Andrews, Mr Frank Colthurst, Mr John Blake Dillon, Mr G. Hendron, Mr James Lenihan, Prof K.B.

Nowlan, Mr Rick Bourke, Prof Thomas Kavanagh, Dr Seamus F. Cahalane, Mr Seamus O'Riain, Mr Andrew Lord, Mr James O'Driscoll, Mr Justice G. Clarke, Sr T. Augustine Barry, Sr M. Arsenius Crowley and Sr Mary Threadgold. The inaugural meeting of the Board was held on 16 January 1978.

The year 1979 was designated Year of the Child. On the feast of St Anthony, 13 June 1979, Bishop Dermot O'Mahony, DD, celebrated Mass for the Hospital's little patients. The occasion attracted a large gathering of staff. In addition, by way of commemorating the Year of the Child, the parishioners of Our Lady of Lourdes Church, Sean McDermott Street, collected a sum of almost £52,000, which they presented to the Casualty Department for the purchase of a cardiac monitor. This gift was very much appreciated by all staff.

THE 1980s

On 12 June 1980, one of Temple Street's greatest benefactors died. Sir William Butlin had been a great friend and supporter of The Children's Hospital. It was through the Variety Club of Ireland that the Sisters of Charity had been initially introduced to Sir William and his wife, Lady Sheila. Over the years, Sir William had provided funds for the building of the X-ray and Pathology Departments.

The Minister for Health, Dr Michael Woods made his first visit to the Hospital on 19 June 1980. He was met by a representative group and later expressed his appreciation for the time afforded him.

On 11 February 1981, the new Theatre Suite and lift were completed and handed over by the builders. The cost of the work was £400,000, of which £300,000 was paid by the Department of Health and the balance by amounts received from the Variety Club of Ireland and other donations. All equipment for the theatres was purchased through grants from the Department of Health.

The 1980s saw one of Temple Street's legendary figures retire. This time it was Miss Elizabeth (Lily) Butler who retired in 1981. She had given forty years of unbroken loyal service as secretary to the hospital. On her retirement, she was presented with the *Benemerenti Medal* as a token of appreciation from the Sisters and staff.

During the decade, services continued to be improved and upgraded. In February 1983 a Laminar Flow Unit was opened on St Michael's C Ward, with the then Minister for Health and Social Welfare, Mr Barry Desmond, TD, in attendance. The generosity of parents, with a donation of £10,000, was remarkable. At the time cancer research funding was £10,000 and a further £20,000 as a donation covered the cost of the Unit.

St Anthony's Hospital, Herbert Avenue, which had opened in 1946 and served as an auxiliary hospital to Temple Street, closed on 7 June 1983. Three patients who remained on the day of closure were transferred to Temple Street. Due to many changes in medicine, distance from Temple Street, cost of bus fares for parents travelling to visit their children, in addition to a great drop in bed occupancy, it sadly became necessary to close the hospital.

On 13 June 1983 the then Minister for Health, Mr Barry Desmond, TD signed an agreement confirming the development of The Children's Hospital on site. Consequently, surrounding sites were purchased which included St George's Hall, Corporation Yard and the Crystal Glass Company. A project team was set up which included Department of Health officials. Regular meetings were held and a brief prepared. However, in the late 1980s it was decided not to develop the Hospital on the Temple Street site, but to use a site on the Mater campus instead.

In January 1985, Mr Justice T.A. Finlay resigned from the chairmanship of the Hospital's Board of Management as he had been appointed Chief Justice of the Supreme Court. Justice Finlay had been chairman from the inception of the Board and had fulfilled his duties with wisdom, skill and dedication.

In the same year on 15 May, Mr James Nugent SC attended his first meeting of the Board as chairman. The Hospital would like to record its appreciation and gratitude to Mr Nugent for his exceptional commitment and guidance through the troubled years of the late eighties until 1993, when he resigned.

Building of a new convent, which began in September 1983, was finally completed in October 1985. All the Sisters were in residence by 25 November 1985. The space occupied by the Sisters in the Hospital was then put at the disposal of the Hospital management. St Anthony's Shrine was also relocated from St Anthony's laneway to a suitable site in the Nurses' Home beside the new convent.

The Child Health Foundation was launched at the end of April 1985 to raise funds for research. A fundraising group, Community Counselling Services, was employed for six months to raise a capital sum. By the time they had completed their contract on 15 November 1985, £612,584 had been pledged.

As was the case in all hospitals in the country, there were major cutbacks in revenue and capital funding during the eighties. By the end of June 1987, 61 staff had left the hospital and the number of beds reduced from 170 to 125, including day beds. However, from a clinical point of view, the heyday of Temple Street occurred during the 1980s, as noted by Prof O'Brien:

> *By 1980, the Hospital has an enormous clinical load, including a Casualty Department which catered for 1000 patients per week. Some 40,000 attended the Outpatient Department and 7000 operations were carried out annually. However, it was clear that as modern paediatric medicine developed, expert consultant personnel were necessary. If there was ever a golden age in Temple Street, it was from 1980 to 1990, during which time a casualty consultant, neurologists, radiologists, specialists in metabolic medicine, specialist pathologists, orthopaedic surgeons, ophthalmologists, specialists in craniofacial surgery and ENT surgery were appointed. Strong links were established with The National Maternity Hospital, and above all with The Mater Hospital. These associations put in place a practical direction for the management of children from birth through adolescence and adulthood – similar to many centres in Europe and the United States.*

EARLY 1990S

In order to to keep pace with medical developments, a number of important developments took place within the hospital during the nineties. In 1993 the mortuary was refurbished and a parent bereavement room was provided. St Michael's B Ward was refurbished in full, with increased accommodation made available for parents. St Brigid's Ward, formerly an Ear, Nose & Throat (ENT) ward, was fully refurbished and reopened for metabolic patients.

Surgical Flat Ward was divided into four-bedded units and modern ancillary facilities provided in 1994. In May of that year, a new Metabolic Outpatient Department was officially opened. Some of the funding was donated by the old St Ultan's Hospital – located on the grounds of Temple Street – from the proceeds of the sale of that hospital. On the occasion of the opening, Dr Eileen Naughten, the consultant in charge of the Unit, paid tribute to Dr Doreen Murphy who started the Metabolic Unit and built it up from the 1960s until the 1980s. Dr Naughten referred to the 'diet for life' policy that Dr Murphy had initiated. Tribute was also paid to parents of children attending the Unit for their support and fundraising efforts over the years.

Other departments refurbished in 1994 included St Patrick's Ward, the Physiotherapy Department, Top Flat Ward, and the Hospital façade. Computerisation of the X-ray Department, Laboratory, Stores, and Pharmacy also took place.

A considerable number of important developments took place in 1995. The former Anthonian Press accommodation was refurbished to house the National Screening Laboratory and Accounts Department. The main lift in the Hospital was replaced and associated alterations to wards also became necessary. Phase one of fire precautions at a cost of £150,000 was carried out, as were improved security measures. Refurbishment of an additional number of wards and the entrance and main hall also took place.

LATE 1990s

The 30th anniversary of the National Metabolic Screening Programme, based in The Children's Hospital, was celebrated by a weeklong conference in March 1996. As part of those celebrations, the formal opening of the new laboratory to house the National Screening Programme was held on 11 March 1996.

In July 1996, a new Outpatients Department, combining the existing Surgical OPD and a major extension, was formally opened by the then Minister for Health, Mr Michael Noonan, TD. The total cost of the project was £800,000, of which £500,000 was provided by the Department of Health. The balance of £300,000 was contributed by the Sisters of Charity.

With the agreement of the Department of Health, in 1996 the Hospital in association with University College Dublin instigated a Postgraduate Diploma Course in Paediatric

Nursing. The first intake of students for this course was in autumn 1996 and it marked the end of the three-year Undergraduate Sick Children's Nursing Course run by the School of Nursing in the Hospital for many years.

A group of Friends of Temple Street formed a voluntary committee in 1996 to petition the Government to build a new hospital for the city of Dublin. Recognising however that the service would have to be maintained, a new team was appointed for the next stage of the hospital's development. That team was as follows: Architects – T.J. Cullen & Co.; Quantity Surveyors – Keogh & McConnell; Structural Engineers – Moloney & Miller; Mechanical & Electrical Engineers – Homan O'Brien. The new design team were asked to prepare plans for:

1. A new A & E Department.

2. A new Day Ward.

3. An MRI Suite.

4. An extension to the Audiology Department.

5. Provision of a new laboratory facility for the National Reference Meningococcal Laboratory.

Architects, T. Fox Associates, were appointed for the refurbishment of the existing Hospital. The planned developments had to be done in the context of maintaining services all the time, bearing in mind the possibility the Hospital would be moving to a new campus.

The programme of upgrading and maintainance of existing services of the Hospital came to fruition in 1996 when the extension to the Audiology Department was completed. An extension to the Audiology Department was completed in 1996 at a cost of £100,000, which was funded by the Department of Health. When the special Audiology Clinic was opened in 1965, the acoustics cost £5,000, funded by the Sisters of Charity. The Children's Hospital was the only hospital in the country providing that service at the time.

(left) Mr Brian Cowen, TD, Minister for Health and Children, with Dr Veronica Donoghue at the official opening of the National Meningococcal Laboratory in 1988; (right) Mr Cowen with laboratory staff at the opening.

In 1998, The Children's Hospital was designated as the National Meningitis Centre and a new laboratory for meningitis screening was built at a cost of £120,000, funded by the Department of Health and Children. Mr Brian Cowen, TD, Minister for Health and Children, performed the opening ceremony in June 1998.

The special unit to house the Magnetic Resonance Imaging Scanner was completed in 2001. An Taoiseach, Mr Bertie Ahern, TD, performed the opening on 2 July 2001 which was attended by a delegation from the Electricity Supply Board who had undertaken a massive fundraising programme for the project.

The development of the Accident and Emergency Department and a new Day Ward commenced in 2000 and was completed in July 2001. Formal opening of the Unit took place on 17 July 2001 by Mr Micheál Martin, TD, Minister for Health and Children.

These developments came about as The Children's Hospital, Temple Street had for a number of years been in negotiations with the Department of Health and Children for the development of a new hospital. Initially, this was agreed to as a development scheme of 'knock and build'. However, the plan was later revoked and the Religious Sisters of Charity entered negotiations with the Religious Sisters of Mercy regarding the purchase of a site on the Mater campus on which to build the new hospital.

Judge Richard Johnson greets An Taoiseach, Mr Bertie Ahern, TD,
at the opening of the Magnetic Resonance Imaging Unit in June 2001.

These negotiations began to take shape under the auspices of the Charity–Mercy joint venture during the late eighties and early nineties. In the context of these earlier discussions, the 'notion' of an exchange of hospitals – under one governance – was raised between the two congregations; the whole purpose of which was to improve the healthcare services under the care of the two congregations in the Dublin area. A direct exchange of trusteeship took place with no disturbance in the operation of any of the hospitals involved.

Thus in a joint initiative by the Sisters of Mercy and the Religious Sisters of Charity, with the relocation of the Children's Hospital to the Mater site, the Sisters of Mercy are now the Trustees of the new Mater campus which will include The Children's Hospital. As part of the National Development Plan, An Taoiseach, Mr Bertie Ahern, TD, announced on 22 November 1999 that the Government would fund the development of the Mater and Children's Hospital at Eccles Street to provide comprehensive healthcare for all age groups. This announcement was welcomed by both hospitals.

*The last Board of Management of The Children's Hospital. Front row (l. to r.): Dr Sheila Macken,
Dr John Murphy, Mr Justice Richard Johnson (chairman), Sr M. Magdalen McPartlan, RSC,
Mr Paul Cunniffe. Back row (l. to r.): Ms Rita O'Shea, Mr Sean Sheehan, Ms Jane O'Connor,
Dr Veronica Donoghue, Ms Mary Finlay Geoghegan, Mr Fionn MacCumhaill, and
Sr Helena McGilly, RSC.*

THE 2000S

The Mater and Children's Hospital Development Company (MCHD) was established
to oversee the new development. Subsequently, on 18 December 2001, the
Development Control Plan was approved by the Minister for Health and Children. And
so the story of The Children's Hospital that had its small beginnings in a house in
Buckingham Street, to its present position in Temple Street, and to its future location in
Eccles Street, goes on.

*Sr M. Magdalen McPartlan, RSC, is local leader of the Religious Sisters of Charity at 1,
Temple Street. Prof Niall O'Brien is a former Consultant Neonatologist at The Children's
Hospital.*

Hospital staff on stand by during the eve of the millennium, 1999/2000.

POST-CENTENARY NURSING

Maria Lynch

THE 1970s

Nursing in the 1970s changed everywhere and Temple Street was no different. Certainly modern medical advances influenced these changes. Survival rates of infants/children, particularly the neonatal mortality rate, improved. Diseases such as cystic fibrosis, metabolic disorders, and others thought to have been hopeless, were now being successfully treated. Improvements in surgery and anaesthesia as well as diagnostic procedures all spurred on changes in nursing techniques and practice.

It became clear that patients responded best to specialised nursing care and therapy. Originally, patients requiring constant care and supervision were 'specialled' on a medical or surgical ward. Nurses became more experienced in the care of critically ill patients, and out of this was born the intensive care nurse. And so in 1972, Temple Street opened its Intensive Care Unit with a bed complement of five.

Other innovations also took place. Orthopaedics recognised the need for a nurse with additional knowledge and skills. The nurse was trained in the techniques of applying plaster of Paris and worked alongside the surgeon in the operating theatre, orthopaedic outpatient clinics and, in particular, fracture clinics. She/he also attended the inpatients and, in particular, postoperative patients. In addition, she/he educated the parents in the care of their child while in plaster, and liaised with parents following discharge.

Parents in general became more involved in the care of their children while in hospital. Visiting time had been extended and there was now open visiting for parents. In 1965 research carried out by Bowlby and later by Robertson (1970) and Hawthorn (1979) as well as the Platt Report (1959) in the UK indicated the benefits of parent's presence during hospitalisation. These findings revolutionised the concept of parents visiting and staying with their infant/child while in hospital. The Association for the Welfare of Children in Hospital (AWCH) was set up in the UK in the 1960s. It also raised awareness of the needs of children in hospital in Ireland and the need for parent facilities. Thus AWCH was established in Ireland in 1970.

Play is an essential element in the transformation of an otherwise formidable setting from home to hospital. While play is everybody's concern in a children's hospital, it is the sick children's nurse who is pivotal in ensuring its provision in conjunction with the play specialist. Play is therefore used by every nurse in gaining the trust of the sick child and in helping to explain procedures to the different age groups. The playroom is used as a 'safe' area in which children can go to play away from the ward area, where unpleasant or painful procedures may have been carried out.

The importance of including the family in helping a child to recover from illness or injury cannot be overlooked. A natural progression from having parents visiting/staying with their child in hospital is the concept of family-centered care, which attempts to meet the emotional, social and developmental needs of children and families in all healthcare settings. In family-centered care, the family is considered to be a partner in the child's care, learning about the child's condition and participating in decisions regarding the child's care. In this way, families gain knowledge and confidence in caring for their child. This is especially necessary today, with early discharge/shorter hospital stay, and in day therapy. In some instances, parents are educated to perform complex procedures at home.

THE 1980S

The 1980s brought further changes at Temple Street. Expansion of the operating theatres took place in 1981 providing three theatre suites. Currently the theatres have been expanded again giving a fourth theatre. This will primarily be used for day surgery, therefore increasing the efficiency of the theatre. It is also acknowledged that parental presence for children undergoing anaesthesia alleviates unnecessary trauma and distress to the child. Parental participation has become increasingly emphasised and an accepted feature in caring for the sick child. A designated nurse now escorts the parents to the anaesthetic room while their child is undergoing induction of anesthesia.

Parent accommodation and parent facilities for parents living in the hospital were first established in the mid-1980s and indeed the facilities have expanded greatly since. The Hospital now has its own accommodation officer, and facilities include kitchen, shower rooms and laundry. Indeed the needs of our parents/families are continuously growing and provide additional challenges for the future.

THE 1990S

This decade has possibly seen the most advances in nursing practice than any other decade of the 20th century. The practice of nursing evolved into a systematic approach to nursing care, grounded in evidence-based practice with family-centered care. It is now based on a systematic problem-solving approach, through assessment of the child, planning of the nursing intervention, implementation of care and the evaluation of the care given. The documentation was developed by using a model of nursing based on the 'Activities of Living' as identified by research undertaken by Roper, Logan & Tierney (1980) and the Nottingham model of care (Smith 1995) which uses two concepts, that of family-centred care and negotiated care on which the nursing care plan is based. This became known as the 'nursing process' and is still in use today. Consequently, the parent actively participates in the care of their infant/child.

The health services underwent change too in this decade, as a result of constant and rapid development in response to technological, social and economic changes both domestically and internationally. Public awareness of health issues and personal expectations of the care received in the health service also increased.

In 1997 a Commission on Nursing was set up to look at the evolving role of nurses, reflecting their professional development and their overall management of service. It also looked at promotional opportunities and at nurse education and training.

The Report of the Commission on Nursing, 'A Blueprint for the Future', was launched on 16 September 1998. It contained a wide range of recommendations for the development of nursing and midwifery as a key profession within the health service. This report has singularly changed nursing forever. Prior to the Report on the

Commission on Nursing, the only opportunities for promotion were the traditional route through management and education. There was no career pathway for nurses wishing to advance their practice in clinical nursing. The Commission recommended the establishment of clinical pathway as the way forward for nursing in the 21st century.

However, these advances had already been achieved in Temple Street, as we recognised the need for specialist posts. Nurses with specialist knowledge and experience were appointed as clinical nurse specialists, thus improving the quality of care to the patient and their families. In 1999, the National Council for the Professional Development of Nursing and Midwifery was established following a recommendation of the Report on the Commission on Nursing. This council established the criteria for the qualification of clinical nurse specialists.

Currently there are nineteen clinical nurse specialist posts, which have been approved by the National Council for the Professional Development of Nursing and Midwifery in Temple Street. There are now clinical nurse specialists in cystic fibroses, asthma, infection control, CPR training, haemovigilence, neurology, dermatology, ENT, ophthamology, diabetes, renal, haemodialysis, haemovigilance orthopaedics, pain management, metabolic and occupational health. Lastly, a new post of child and adolescent health nurse specialist was created.

The traditional titles of nurses have also been replaced. For example, the titles 'senior ward sister', or 'junior ward sister', are no longer in use. Nurses are now recognised as clinical nurse managers with level CNM1, CNM2 and a new grade of CNM3, which is a higher grade, appointed to specialised areas of high acuity. Clinical facilitators also have been appointed in four key areas of the hospital. Their role is to facilitate educational learning and give support to post-registration students, undergraduate students in their paediatric secondment from their general degree programme, and newly appointed staff nurses.

The 1990s saw further developments in Temple Street, where nurses became ever more skilled. A Telemetry Unit was incorporated in Top Flat medical ward in 1996. It allowed children to have continuous EEG monitoring with close circuit video recording of seizure activity at the same time. It is the first Paediatric Telemetry Unit in the country. The Intensive Care Unit was expanded to include a four-bedded High

Dependency Unit in 1999. A Paediatric Intensive Care Course for nurses has now been established. This is the first Higher Diploma in Nursing Studies/Paediatric Intensive Care for nurses and is affiliated to University College Dublin.

During the 1990s, change also came in the form of nursing attire. Uniforms changed in accordance with the identified needs of health and safety. Tunic and trousers replaced the dress and caps of the past.

Prior to 1998, sick children's nursing had three means of entry; (1) a three-year direct entry course, i.e. for school leavers; (2) a four-year integrated course with St Vincent's Hospital, Elm Park. This was sick children's nursing combined with general training where the students spent time in both hospitals, and at the end of the course they undertook exams in both disciplines. They were then dual qualified as RSCN and RGN; (3) a postgraduate course of initially thirteen-months duration, which was later extended to eighteen months. The nurse was already a registered nurse on one of the divisions of the nurse's register of An Bord Altranais.

In 1989, an EU Directive on nursing failed to recognise the singular qualification of mental handicap, psychiatric and sick children's nursing. The Department of Health and Children recognised that nurses with singular qualifications in these specialties would be at a disadvantage regarding employment. Moreover, the Department considered that all Irish-trained nurses should have equal employment opportunities outside of Ireland. As a result, the Department recommended that the three-year course for RSCN be discontinued and replaced by a post-registration course of eighteen months. This occurred in 1998. As with all changes, there was a cost implication since the three-year students were now post-registration students. The number of students was reduced from one hundred direct entry student to seventy-five post-registration. The shortfall was then taken up by the appointment of ward attendants, which was a new grade of staff for Temple Street.

In 1996, the post-registration course was changed to a Higher Diploma in Sick Children's Nursing and affiliated to University College Dublin. The duration of the course is eighteen months at present.

Nursing management structure has also changed and expanded. The director of nursing is part of the senior hospital management team and involved in the strategic planning and development of the Hospital. He/she is a member of the Hospital Executive Committee, and since 1993 is a member of the Board of Management.

The assistant directors of nursing are responsible for the management of specific clinical areas and nurse specialists. They are responsible for the development of nursing policies, planning and committees. Also, providing overall supervision of the nursing service including day-to-day management and after hour's management of the Hospital as a whole. This is carried out on a 24-hour, 365-day basis.

Last group of graduating nurses from The Children's Hospital, 2002.

THE 2000S

At the turn of the century came the long awaited new Accident & Emergency Department and a new Day Ward. The Day Ward was expanded to a twenty-bedded unit, including medical and surgical patients and their families. Another development has been the introduction of paediatric haemodialysis. Children had previously been dialysed in adult haemodialysis units. This service has been further developed and is currently providing a six-day haemodialysis service. To this end triage nursing has been introduced. The first Higher Diploma in Nursing Studies/Accident and Emergency for nurses affiliated to University College Dublin was also established in 2001.

Nursing is constantly changing and providing challenges as we face the future. All challenges are willingly undertaken as we endeavour to provide continuous improvement in quality of care for our patient and their families.

Ms Maria Lynch is Assistant Director of Nursing at The Children's Hospital.

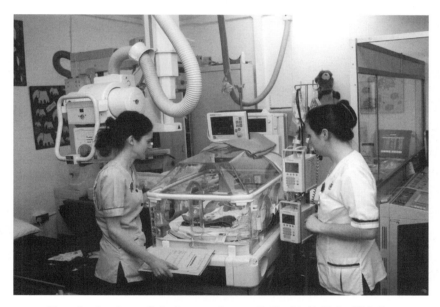

Veronica Lambert, clinical nurse educator (left) with Siobhán O'Malley,
postgraduate student nurse (right) in the Neonatal Department.

MISSION IN HEALTHCARE

SR AGNES REYNOLDS, RSC

Every great work for humanity has arisen from a need perceived and understood. Scarcely could there be greater needs than those of the poor in the 19th century.

The story of the foundation of the Religious Sisters of Charity Health Service is bound up with the story of an even more unusual venture. This was the founding of St Vincent's Hospital in 1834, the first Catholic Voluntary Hospital in Ireland to be opened, managed and staffed by a religious congregation of women. Still less should be forgotten the spirit that inspired it, the spirit of one of the great humanitarian figures of the 19th century, Mary Aikenhead. To understand the spirit of this great woman, we must know something of her life and of the Ireland that she loved.

Mary Aikenhead was born on 19 January 1787 in the city of Cork. She was the eldest daughter of Mary Stackpole, a Catholic, the daughter of a prominent city merchant, and Dr David Aikenhead, a Protestant of Scottish descent. Dr Aikenhead made one stipulation. Though his wife should be free to practice her own religion, it was to be fully understood that if they had children, they should be brought up as members of the Protestant religion. In due course she was baptised and given the name, Mary. Then in her infancy, Dr Aikenhead made a strange decision. He placed his cherished baby in fosterage with a family of devout Catholics, John and Mary Rorke who lived in a neat thatched cottage on Eason's Hill, an almost rural area of Cork famed for its bracing air. Like their neighbours they were poor, decent folk, happy to secure a frugal livelihood from their humble trades, despite their privations. It was here that baby Mary grew to childhood. So well did she thrive, sharing their simple life that Dr Aikenhead left her in the care of the Rorkes until she was six-years-old. This period of her life is significant in that it allowed her to know the poor as people. She grew to love them and from this flamed an attitude of respect, of dignity and deep concern for their welfare – an attitude which characterised her entire life and with which, in time, she imbued her young congregation.

At length the time came when Mary had to return to her city home. Her distress at parting with Mary and John Rorke was lessened by Dr Aikenhead's request that they move to the Aikenhead household to continue their care of Mary and the other younger children born into the family.

Mary now grew up in the social surroundings of the Grand Parade, the affluent part of Cork city. She began to accompany her father in his carriage to Shandon Church on Sundays. Some years later, she felt drawn to the faith that she had unconsciously learned in the Rorke's cottage. Yet, she feared to cause her dearly loved father any pain.

Mary started to visit the Bishop's Chapel with her grandmother, Mrs Stackpole. A strong attachment also grew with her widowed aunt, Mrs Gorman, both of whom were fervent Catholics. Mary frequently joined them going to Mass. Soon she made excuses for absenting herself from church at Shandon and began to go alone to the Chapel to attend Mass in the mornings. It was at the South Chapel in Cork in 1802 that the seed of the congregation of the Sisters of Charity was sown when Mary Aikenhead listened to the sermon on Dives and Lazarus. The disinterested attitude of the rich man and the suffering of the poor man made such an impression on her that she immediately resolved to do something to uplift the poor, to enable them to realise their worth and dignity.

Mother Mary Aikenhead.

At the age of fifty, Dr Aikenhead decided to retire from his practice. His retirement was of short duration. By the end of 1801, he was gravely ill with no hope of recovery. However, on 18 December 1801, he was received into the Catholic Church on his deathbed. Six months later on 6 June 1802, his well-loved daughter, Mary, became a Catholic after serious study and preparation.

Our Mission is to bring the healing love of Christ in liaison with the communities we serve, to all sick children and their families, in the spirit of the foundress of the Sisters of Charity, Mary Aikenhead. In our friendly and caring environment, we strive to promote the highest quality of care for all with dignity, compassion and respect. We value our staff and encourage their development.

David Aikenhead's influence on his daughter's life cannot be ignored. She saw his kindness to the poor of every class and creed. He gladly assented to her requests for this or that medicine for her poor friends on Eason's Hill. With a young friend, Cecilia Lynch, she made morning rounds through the back lanes and streets of Cork, bringing relief to the sick and poor. This strengthened her decision to devote her life to the relief and rehabilitation of the poor and to vow herself to this work in religious life.

During her visits with a friend, Mrs Anna Maria O'Brien in Dublin, she was introduced to a priest, Fr Daniel Murray, who later became Archbishop of Dublin. His idea of religious sisters who would be free to visit the sick and poor in their homes was similar to hers. Mary Aikenhead was a woman with a big heart, but also a keen mind and great vision. She realised that unorganised charity could do little as a lasting remedy to ignorance and poverty. With a companion, Alicia Walsh, she spent some years in formation in the Institute of the Blessed Virgin Mary, York, and on 22 August 1815, Mary Aikenhead founded the Congregation of the Religious Sisters of Charity *for the service of the poor and especially the sick poor.*

From September 1816, this first group of religious women in Ireland not to be bound by the law of enclosure, tramped the streets of Dublin serving their poor neighbours from their own slender resources. To serve the poor in every way was to be their life's work.

At a profession ceremony in 1817, Fr Peter Kenny SJ preached a homily taking as his text the words of St Paul (Cor. 2:17), *Caritas Christi Urget Nos* – the love of Christ drives us. Mary Aikenhead took this text as her motto. This continues to be the motto of the Sisters of Charity and is encompassed in their crest.

Close familiarity with the lives of the poor, their miseries and lack of medical care made Mary conceive of the idea of a hospital where the poor could receive the care that the rich could buy for money. Her submission in 1833 to 'The Commission of Enquiry into the Conditions of the Irish Poor' made uncomfortable reading. It was a challenge to the status quo from an early apostle of social justice. She ends with regrets that '*we have not the means to erect a hospital.*' Then Providence stepped in. Mary Aikenhead found herself with £3000 at her disposal and promptly purchased, through friends, the Earl of Meath's mansion on St Stephen's Green.

A hundred years later in 1934, Dr Bill Doolin was to write in the Centenary Records:

> *Others must have seen the need even as she saw it but, less daring, forbade to fill it...hers be the credit for her divine recklessness.*

The foundation of St Vincent's Hospital on St Stephen's Green in 1834 marked the beginning of the Sisters of Charity Health Service. For more than a century and a half, the Sisters of Charity and their co-workers have played a vital role in healthcare in Ireland carrying forward to the present day the *Mission* begun by Mary Aikenhead.

Sr Agnes Reynolds is Director of Mission of the Religious Sisters of Charity.

The last three Sisters of Charity involved in Temple Street, left to right, Sr Anne Curry, Sr Ann Forrest and Sr Mary Magdalen McPartlan.

ST ANTHONY'S BREAD

ANNALS OF ST JOSEPH'S HOSPITAL

St Anthony's Shrine at Temple Street.

[The year] *1872 saw the opening of The Children's Hospital in Temple Street. Financially, the hospital depended entirely on voluntary subscriptions and fundraising activities such as bazaars and fetes. In time, the donations sent to the hospital with requests for prayers for special needs and intentions became known as donations for St Anthony's Bread. The devotion of St Anthony's Bread was officially launched in the hospital in August 1895 and a few months later the Association of St Anthony of Padua was established. The aims of the Association were: to cultivate and spread devotion to St Anthony and secondly, to provide bread for the poor.*

The Temple Street Association became affiliated to the Universal Association of St Anthony based in Padua. The members participate in the many spiritual benefits attached to the Universal Association. The Temple Street office is the official centre of the devotion in Ireland.

In the early years of the Hospital's existence, bread, clothes and other necessities were distributed to the sick children of the poor through the outpatients department. The service has expanded. There are now two offices dealing with correspondence and donations and a considerable amount of money finds its way into St Anthony's Fund for the Poor each year. The fund is devoted exclusively to the needs of sick children and their families. While the hospital is now supported by State aid, the St Anthony's Fund provides facilities and services beyond the capacity of the grants provided by the State.

'

Extract from Annals of St Joseph's Hospital, Temple Street (May 1894 to May 1900).
Provided by Sr Martha Magdalen Power, Sister-in-Charge, St Anthony's Shrine at The Children's Hospital.

2

STAFF
RECOLLECTIONS

MacAuley Connection

Mr Patrick MacAuley

The MacAuley family connection with the Sisters of Charity extended over many decades. It began in 1911, when my father was appointed surgeon to The Children's Hospital. He was a great friend of Sr Mary Polycarp; a friendship that lasted for many years. Indeed when Cappagh Hospital was opened, my father advised Sr Mary Polycarp on the staff arrangements. However, on his appointment as a senior surgeon to the Mater Hospital in 1920, he had to retire from all other hospital appointments. He was then succeeded in Temple Street and Cappagh by his brother, Harry MacAuley.

On my appointment in 1955, I maintained the family connection, and worked there until 1989 and also in Cappagh over the same period. At that time, there was no payment, except for what you earned in private practice. When the 'pool payments' came into force in 1959, there were tremendous disputes among staff members on how it was to be divided. Mother Canisius, who was the Sister Superior at the time, instructed me to look after the interests of the senior members, and I was subsequently appointed to the Medical Board of the Hospital.

In relation to orthopaedics and specialisation, Frank Duff was there just before me but he was a general surgeon with a special interest in urology. In fact, all the general surgeons were doing all forms of surgery. I was appointed as a full-time orthopaedic surgeon and the first thing I had to do was organise the treatment of all orthopaedics and musculoskeletal trauma. As this was a matter to be handled delicately, I briefed the Sisters and my father's great friend and associate, John Shanley. Over a period of time, I took over the outpatient fractures and subsequently all orthopaedics. Orthopaedic patients were mainly transferred to Cappagh for long-stay care. With advances, paediatric orthopaedics hospital stay was considerably reduced and we were able to resume a significant input in paediatric orthopaedics in Temple Street, as Cappagh moved more and more into the adult sphere.

For the first ten or more years of my tenure, I was on my own but my colleague Niall Mulvihill in the Mater used to stand in for me on a voluntary basis. Another great helper in the real sense – looking after things for me and doing all sorts of odd jobs – was the famous Paddy Doyle. He himself admitted that, 'I was the only man who came to work in Temple Street before [Mr MacAuley] in the morning.'

Another particular interest I had in Temple Street was the development of day care surgery. With the increasing emphasis on children leaving hospital as soon as possible with their parents, I got involved and treated many of my paediatric patients as day cases. It was fascinating, though everybody was against it – the nursing staff were worried about it bringing in infection, the anaesthetists were worried about giving children anaesthetics and letting them go home that afternoon, everybody was up in uproar. Indeed one nurse, having observed me looking for appropriate space in the Hospital, ran up to Sr Ann Eucharia and said, 'Oh Sister, there's a man from the Eastern Health Board inspecting our lavatories to see if they are suitable – or something or other, I'd be afraid of him.' Luckily, Sr Ann Eucharia reassured her.

My main supporter in instituting day care surgery was Sister Elsie Mallon in St Michael's B Ward. She came and informed me that she would love to *try* the day care work. Of course, under her supervision, it was a great success.

As I had started on my own in 1955, I was happy that on leaving in 1989, Temple Street had four orthopaedic surgeons and it became far and away, the largest paediatric orthopaedic unit in the country, and remains so. Midway through my time there, Mother Canisius arrived as Mother Rectress and was a tower of strength, and in turn a great supporter of mine. She generally was 'on top of everything'. It was a great pleasure to work with her. And, of course, it was also a tremendous pleasure to work with Sr Ann Eucharia in her 'many roles', and that great man, friend and supporter, John Shanley.

Mr Patrick MacAuley was Consultant Orthopaedic Surgeon at The Children's Hospital from 1955 to 1989.

MEMORIES OF PADDY DOYLE
HEAD PORTER 1940–1991

JOHN DOYLE
ANNE O'CONNOR

It is only in the modern world of today that we realise that tasks so run of the mill but an essential part of hospital life in Paddy's time, would in fact come to shape the importance of the hospital's reliance on its head porter. Indeed it showed the major contribution Paddy made to Temple Street.

I'm sure many people have different memories of various incidents, whether funny or serious, human or personal. Daily duties for Paddy would involve cleaning fires and replacing coal buckets, running the generator, pumping the oil for the boilers and cleaning, making tea for the consultants and many trips to the kitchen to collect and deliver special delph for the parlours.

The annual Hospital Ball and sales of work, organising taxis and the visit of the Lord Mayor on Christmas Day were just a small portion of his duties, but of which I have fond memories. Others include Friday afternoons when there was a major exodus of staff going home, in particular, nurses, many of whom would require a taxi to get them to the train or bus station. Paddy would regularly see them off from the front steps, like a commissioner in one of the large hotels, ensuring the taxis had arrived so everyone got to their required destinations on time.

Paddy had a magnificent rapport with the local residents and if there was any trouble with any children, he could talk to their parents in his own way. Result – problem solved!

Switched on – Paddy Doyle with Valerie Flynn at the switchboard.

The Hospital Ball was the highlight of the Hospital's social calendar. Paddy's attire for the night was to wear a green jacket. It is said that he wore his green jacket more than most of the wining golfers have worn the green jacket at Augusta, Georgia.

I am constantly reminded of one particular incident which possibly describes Paddy to a tee. A courier had arrived to collect a package located in the laboratory. Paddy went out to the back steps, whistled up to a window and started to flap his arms. In no time at all, the package had been delivered to the front hall to the waiting courier. By the way, the name of the courier company was 'Wings'. His methods were so simple, yet produced the perfect results.

It is now over a decade since Paddy left the Hospital, but his name will live forever in hospital folklore, in particular, his dedication to ensuring that the patient was the most important factor in the Hospital, and that all of us should never lose sight of this fact. His shining light will never burn out.

The son of Paddy Doyle, John Doyle is Head Porter at The Children's Hospital.

John Doyle, head porter.

'ROUNDING UP THE POSSE'

I have so many memories of Paddy but one story in particular always comes to mind. Not long after I began working in Temple Street in 1981, we started to be paid by cheque, which meant that staff had to go to the bank to cash them. The climate throughout Dublin City at the time was one of rising petty crime, particularly bag snatches. Many staff were anxious about carrying a lot of cash back from the bank. Of course, it was Paddy to the rescue! He organised us into small groups or 'posses'. Paddy would do the ring around, and we would all gather at the front hall from where he would walk us over and back from the bank. Now Paddy was no giant in size, but the respect he had throughout the local area kept us all safe and secure.

Ms Anne O'Connor is a member of the Medical Records staff.

'CUPPA' SUPPORT

SR TERESA EUCHARIA, RSC

I was appointed to the Casualty Department in The Children's Hospital in 1951. At that time, the Casualty and Outpatient Unit worked under one administration. However, after some years, the Casualty Department became a separate unit.

The surrounding area of the Casualty Department and other parts of Temple Street were in a great state of poverty, unemployment and hardships of all kinds. Families found it very difficult to cope. It was a very challenging time in Casualty dealing with those conditions as well as the numbers of sick children attending each day. It also made the workload very acute and extra busy. I was always impressed with the patience, caring and goodness of the medical and nursing staff, sometimes stretched to the limit of long working hours and being exceptionally busy with emergencies.

The times were interesting, sad and sometimes amusing. Casualty was a refuge for the children from Temple Street, and later Hardwicke Street. They had no outlet or much playing facilities. So one great adventure was on hearing the Dublin Fire Brigade Ambulance siren, a small army of children would run pitter patter after it and then explore around the emergency area. As Casualty was kept busy with emergencies, this venture could take place several times a day. These children were constant visitors with smaller ailments, so a relationship was set up between doctors, nurses and myself with them. Of course, they gained from that friendship very often.

Another very interesting feature of Casualty was the relationship with the houses down at the back of the Outpatients Department – tenements and later the flats, opposite the Hospital. We took a great interest in these people combined with the goodwill and help of house officers and nursing staff. The conditions of some residents living alone were miserable. Once I was requested to assist a poor old lady for transfer to St James's

Hospital; she lived alone and had no relatives. We were her only friends. I remember trying to help her pack her few belongings, ankle deep in water. I did not realise that in giving her particulars to the Admissions Unit she gave my name as next-of-kin. I received a phone call from the Casualty Sister in St James's that evening asking me was I really 'next-of-kin'. I explained the situation to her. Her response was, 'Do you realise, Sister, that the patient had £4,000 in notes around her body?' I had no idea. Of course, the dear old lady only allowed me to put her few small items together.

Sr Teresa Eucharia, RSC.

There were many sad experiences of a similar nature. A particular one comes to mind. I was an assistant in 'laying out' a very elderly lady in the flats opposite the Hospital when a very large sum of money was found by her relatives in a feather pillow. How sad that her life was so poor and miserable when she could have been comfortable. I mention these situations to show that Casualty was unique in the kindness and help to those around the area, as much as treating all children's ailments and emergencies in a very busy Department.

During my time in Casualty we had some very happy days mixed in with days of grief, one of the greatest losses being the death of a child. It was a good sense of achievement being able in some little way to comfort and sustain parents and families. At times one felt hopeless to say or do anything, just our presence with those grieving families was all we could do. I could not speak highly enough of the medical and nursing staff and others in their caring attitude, especially the nursing staff. Their love, patience and nursing of the children was wonderful. It was a great privilege to be part of this group of carers. They also had a great sense of humour, which is so essential for the morale and well-being of those working in a sick children's emergency area. We were blessed to have a good kitchen in the area when, during the trauma of a tragic accident of a child, the warmth and support of a 'cuppa' was very helpful to relatives and they always remarked on the same afterwards. We always kept in mind that such moments were very traumatic for medical and especially nursing staff, so a break with a 'cuppa' was a very welcome token indeed.

Sr Francis Regis was the first social worker in the hospital. Certainly, her coming made an enormous difference to the whole caring system. She excelled in helping families of sick children around the area. She impressed me very much with her theory; first, try and find out the reasons why families are in such conditions, then give the appropriate help.

In reviewing my years spent in Casualty many occasions come to mind. Many times, unfortunately, it was the incidence of cot deaths; those were clearly traumatic. It was so impossible to explain to grief-stricken parents that the cause was not known. Those times have left a memory that will never fade away. It was an occasion of silently being present with them throughout it all. We felt helpless, unable to understand ourselves the trauma of those sudden deaths. Major research has been done and medical staff have studied in great depth the possible causative factors, but it is still a mystery. How often did I hear – 'Sister, he or she was such a healthy baby, never sick in a serious way; was perfect going to bed.' During the night or morning death had struck. It is difficult to imagine the trauma, utter disbelief for parents on those occasions. There were so many over the years, too numerous to mention. Time was not a factor, it could occur when the mother was preparing a meal or at any other time of the day or night.

One Christmas morning, a Dublin Fire Brigade driver, well known to us, was in Casualty with relatives and he said to me, 'It is myself this time.' It was his child, a beautiful baby. On another occasion, the Casualty doctor who had helped so many relatives in similar circumstances was the father of a child brought in to Casualty. He told me that on that day there were five doctors in his house, home for Christmas, and they could do nothing. Staff need great support and help on occasions such as those.

Another poignant scene was the bombing in Dublin in May 1974. Parents were frantically looking for missing children. We had three little girls brought in dead who could only be identified by the ribbons in their hair. Another evening, a Sister and myself were leaving Casualty when the ambulance sounded. We waited and saw a huge telephone box with a child screaming on top of it coming in the door. Someone had tried to make a slit in the box to get out money. A girl had put her hand in and, of course, could not get it out. She was surrounded by telephone staff and garda, because the kiosk had to be uprooted. Many hours went by to try and set her hand free unharmed.

Numerous events come to mind, too many to report. Through it all, I found it a great privilege to be associated with the parents, children and staff. It was wonderful to be able to help families even in a little way to cope with the sickness of children. It was also a great joy to help and support the children in surrounding areas. They were very happy years in spite of the trauma of Casualty. A special mention of the support of my own religious community in so many events must be made. I trust that the great work will continue in caring for the sick children for many more years, especially in the new location of the Hospital.

Sr Teresa Eucharia, RSC, is a former A&E Sister-in-Charge at The Children's Hospital.

An Taoiseach, Mr Bertie Ahern, presenting toys made by prisoners on community service to Sr M. Magdalen McPartlan on behalf of The Children's Hospital at Christmas 2001.

I REMEMBER, WHEN...

MAURA BRIEN

Around 1975, Bridie Elliott asked me to come in for an interview for the canteen. I started on the following Sunday and became a 'jack of all trades'. But I have great memories of Temple Street.

One memory that stands out is of Bridie, who worked in Surgical Flat in the seventies when the Dublin football team was very popular. On Sundays, she would trace in the Dublin colours on the brushes and hoover, and the children loved it. When she came into the ward, the children would say, 'Good morning, Rover' – she had different names on the hoover!

Sr Ann Eucharia always told the staff in the canteen to 'look after the nurses'. We used to sing with the Sisters at evening prayer too. When the Assembly Hall was there, I would join the Sisters and Chaplain for a choir practice of Christmas carols. This was a special event, and at around 8 pm the staff would come from all the departments when the place was decorated. I remember Nancy McHale saying that they borrowed lanterns from the Meath Hospital and Dublin Corporation for the carol singing.

We had great fun doing rehearsals for the annual pantomime. Once, I had a part in *Cinderella* – two of the doctors were the ugly sisters and Paddy Mulhair's wife, Anne, was Cinderella. Overall, a lovely homely atmosphere existed in Temple Street, where everyone knew everybody.

Nancy also has the unforgettable memory of a mouse who ran across the ward one night. She climbed on top of a glass table and shrieked until Sr Mary Arsenius came on the scene. In those days the Sisters' bedrooms were on the same floor as Top Flat. Sr Mary Arsenius could even recognise the children who cried during the night. Nancy also remembers the anguish of student nurses who had to pay for any breakages they had caused – the result being they did not get any pay for months!

There is also another lovely memory which is a tribute to the staff concerned. Some parents, on arriving in Casualty, would go back home (with their sick child), if Peter Keenan and Statia Brennan were not on duty.

There were many funny occasions too numerous to mention. I remember Adele O'Connor in Admissions asking a parent – 'what religion?' The answer came loud and clear – 'Irish'. One time, Adele's heartstrings were pulled when a poor woman told her how much she needed a pram for her child. Adele called on her friends and before long she had acquired a beautiful pram for the woman. Not many days later, however, Adele met her coming up Gardiner Street, with 'the messages' piled high on the pram!

Maura Brien is a former member of the Catering Staff.

A SPECIALTY IS BORN

Mr Daniel G. Kelly

Paediatric urology became a subspecialty in The Children's Hospital around 1956 under the care of Mr Frances Arthur Duff. Previously, Frank had been a general surgeon and some of the work he did in that field still lives on. Particularly, it can be seen in relation to some cleft palates he did as a young surgeon, and indeed he received extremely satisfactory functional cosmetic results. Prior to that time, some neurology was carried out by the various general surgeons attending the Hospital. In 1956 Frank began the development of paediatric urology in The Children's Hospital. He was one of the first subspecialised surgeons in this field in the country.

He was also, of course, attached to St Vincent's Hospital and like a lot of the staff of Temple Street at the time, they had joint appointments in both St Vincent's and The Children's Hospital. It was on similar lines that I joined the staff in 1969 with a commitment to both hospitals. At this stage, Frank had built up an extensive Urology Department and had a large referral of complex urological problems from all over the country. It was a new specialty, evolving rapidly.

There has always been great debate as to who should do paediatric urology – should it be done by the paediatric surgeons who are training in urology or by the adult urologists who have trained in paediatric urology? All that can be said along this line is that whoever does it, needs to be properly trained in the urological discipline. The advantage of the urologist doing the work is that a lot of these patients have very complex problems that follow them all their lives. And so at fourteen years of age, the patient does not have to change to a new surgeon.

Paediatric urology is also very much about teamwork and involves many other disciplines. These include, nephrology, plastics, orthopaedics, general paediatric surgery and neurosurgery. We are very fortunate at The Children's Hospital in that all of these disciplines are available to us. Mr Duff himself was a great team player and he played a mayor part in the development of paediatric urology within the Hospital.

When I started in 1969 there was no Comhairle na nÓspidéal and job descriptions were very limited. Payment was also limited by 'Pools' and 'OPD Sessions'. To a certain extent one had to develop one's own job, and for me this was made much easier by working with such a delightful colleague as Frank Duff.

I recall my first day at the Hospital. Mr Duff had a large list and I set about giving him a hand with it and Dr N. Gumbrielle, who was the anaesthetist and a most pleasant person too. The list was a long one and took a considerable period of time. Unknown to me, Mother Canisius (then Reverend Mother) had arranged a special lunch to introduce me to the House staff. Unfortunately, because of the list, I never got to the lunch. As Reverend Mother, Mother Canisius was certainly a very capable lady. She had a great vision of the development and progress of an institution and at that time, the Hospital was going through a certain valley period with the setting up of a major paediatric hospital on the southside of the city. She brightened up The Children's Hospital in many ways and developed various facilities which were for the good of everybody, and often without seeking full approval from the appropriate authorities!

Frank and I worked side by side in the Outpatients, in Theatre and we shared a number of beds in the Hospital. We were able to cope adequately with the workload but paediatric urology did develop significantly during this period. At that time, there was great emphasis on urinary tract infection in children and screening had become popular in the United States of young schoolgirls between the age of five and fourteen years. With the help of Seamus Cahalane, we set up a screening programme for young girls in the North City, and our figures coincided totally with those achieved elsewhere in various screening programmes in the world. This did bring a further increasing workload to our Department. It is interesting to note that we started the screening with the help of a part-time nurse, a motor scooter and very limited facilities. Later on, through the generosity of the Variety Club of Ireland, we were able to get a motorised van and this helped us to continue with the programme. In particular I would like to recall the truism and generosity of its ex-Chief Barker, Rick Burke. Rick had a very interesting philosophy about The Children's Hospital. He specifically said the Hospital was situated in a large deprived area of the city and needed support from outside. As a result of this increased workload, paediatric urology got three operating sessions per week and three Outpatients.

It is impossible to practice paediatric urology without immediate support from other departments, in particular Radiology and Pathology. It has been very encouraging to see the support we have received from both these departments and to see their tremendous evolution over the last thirty to forty years in the Hospital. Originally, there was only one operating theatre, now there are four very well-equipped theatres and the Outpatient Department of course has been rebuilt into a modern outpatient unit.

The Children's Hospital has always played a major part in teaching with a significant undergraduate commitment to both UCD and the Royal College of Surgeons. Postgraduate level also is a continuant. Specifically, in relation to postgraduate teaching in urology, currently through Frank Duff's work, we were recognised as an appropriate area for training senior registrars in paediatric urology. We must, of course, remember that Mr Duff was president of the Royal College of Surgeons in 1972. The structure of consultant posts has changed down through the years and the present posts are made up primarily of sessional commitment. When this was established in the early 1990s, it became clear that Mr Duff's commitment was far too excessive and so he left the Paediatric Urology Department and I was left to carry on. There are many children, now adults, in Ireland who owe a debt of gratitude to Frank Duff for his great surgical skill and dexterity. Sadly, Frank died in 1998.

The work of the Urology Department continued and, in fact, there has been some reduction in the open surgical commitment because of the evolution of the so-called STING procedure for ureteric reflux. Nevertheless, there are still many other conditions for which we continue to be a very active Paediatric Urological Department that now has two part-time urologists.

The evolution of Day Care has been very important, and it must be remembered that 80–90 per cent of paediatric surgery can now be done as a day case. The Children's Hospital has been to the fore in this development.

At consultant level, I was the last official link between St Vincent's Hospital and The Children's Hospital. The original hospital was mainly staffed by consultants from St

Vincent's Hospital, however, the hospital's geographical position and close proximity to the Mater Hospital and the Rotunda Hospital and the dwindling number of Religious Sisters make it logical to let geography play a major role in the further development of the Hospital. As to the relocation of Hospital on the Mater site, it is very important that The Children's Hospital should retain its own identity and I quote from John Shanley's article in the Centenary Book when he refers to the Royal Commission in 1885 which says:

> *No advantage would be gained on the ground of economy by having Temple Street's little patients treated in the general hospitals of the capital. Children's disease should be treated in sub specialist hospitals.*

Before I conclude, I would like to comment on the warmth and compassion of the nursing care in The Children's Hospital. In my practice, I have experienced it and it is made all the more special, considering that the Hospital deals primarily with a less affluent society. On a personal note, my own son was a patient in the Hospital for several days when he was seriously ill, and I would like to record my extreme gratitude to the nursing staff and Sisters for their care of him on that occasion, and to say what wonderful care they delivered.

Mr Daniel G. Kelly was Consultant Urologist at The Children's Hospital and retired in 2001 with over thirty years of service.

'JUST KEEP SERVING AND SMILING'

KAY MAGUIRE

I came to Temple Street in 1973 to help Sr Ann Eucharia out for a week, and it ran into a month, and then longer, and that's how it started. I must say I had many happy years in Temple Street. It was not like a job; it was a big house with a large family. At the time, Miss Lily Butler was the hospital secretary and administrator. She treated everybody with the greatest of respect, irrespective of job. You worked six days a week, and seven if they were short, but you didn't mind because there was such a happy atmosphere. You felt you were important to the place and the place was important to you.

The consultants in those days were Mr MacAuley, Prof Kavanagh and Dr Doreen Murphy – there were only a few of them. The ward sisters and staff nurses, which I saw coming in as PTS, were lovely girls. We had so many funny times together and I can still see some of them here. We had three catering officers before our present one, Mr Derek Branigan. I worked with him for twenty-five years and found him to be a gentleman. Then there was Paddy in the front desk, and Joan on the switch, Reverend Mother, Miss Butler, Mrs Finn and Mrs Maguire – they were all the people that had their titles!

There is so much you could say about Temple Street in those years, you could make a film from it. Once when Sir William Butlin came to a reception in Temple Street they put on a beautiful meal for him. It seems funny afterwards, but it wasn't at the time. While we were serving the meal, the floor went from under Miss Gilmore (the dietician at the time), and her leg went down through the floorboards. But Miss Butler quickly responded, 'Don't panic girls, just keep serving and smiling.' Miss Gilmore wasn't badly hurt, but we thought it extremely funny.

Temple Street has done some wonderful work for so many children and you got to know very sincere people. I remember how the parents of children involved in road accidents would be devastated, and they would be sent down to the canteen for us to give them tea, and in those days you could have a little cigarette too. You would talk to them and calm them down – everybody looked after everybody else.

The refurbished Catering Department in November 2001.

In my time I saw five accountants come and go. We used to have great fun comparing wages, as in those days it was all done by hand. You would laugh at some of the things, like when the women were broke, and wouldn't have a penny in the middle of the week, and with a house and small children to keep. But they would go to the Wages Department, and the staff would see what they could do for them. If you had a problem and you went to see Miss Butler, she would make time to see you. And by the time she was finished talking to you, your problem never seemed as bad.

Sr Ann Eucharia as a very young Reverend Mother was strict, but she was good. No matter what, if you had to do something, you did it right or did not do it at all. She had her say and it was over and done with.

When Eileen Clear was the cook, we always had very plain food, but plenty of it! Some christened me 'Mother Maguire' – why, I do not know. But if there was anything I could have done for Temple Street, I would have gladly done it. My two daughters worked there, one for twelve years and the other on and off, helping out. Their memories like mine are also very happy. I enjoyed my stay and only wish I hadn't had to retire!

Mrs Kay Maguire is a former member of the Catering Staff.

THE OLD WARRIOR

JOHN SHANLEY (1895–1996)

JOY FITZGERALD

There's no doubt that John Shanley lived in exciting times. In 1923, shortly after the foundation of the State, he was appointed assistant paediatric surgeon to Temple Street Hospital and St Mary's Cappagh, having graduated from University College Dublin in 1919. It was an appointment he held for an entire lifetime, and which ensured he went down in the annals of the Hospital as one of its greatest and most devoted servants. He was a contemporary and personal friend of many of those in power, and he quickly became involved in the National Health Council, precursor to Comhairle na nÓspidéal, in order to advise the Minister on medical issues. In those days, doctors had more direct access to the centre of power than nowadays, and Seán T. O'Ceallaigh used to say, 'I have two ears, John. With one I listen to the Civil Service and with the other, I listen to you.' Between them, by trial and error, they began carving out the foundations of the modern health services.

A loyal son of the city of Dublin, John Shanley was born in 1895 and brought up in Parnell Street from where he attended the O'Connell Schools. He experienced at first hand the events of 1916, when as a medical student he witnessed the first shot of the Rising as he walked home from Mass in the Pro-Cathedral on Easter Monday.

In his early years at the Hospital, social conditions in the city were appalling. The tenements adjacent to Temple Street were teeming with malnourished and underprivileged children. Mr Shanley saw them all in his outpatients. There were no subspecialties then; broken bones, sore throats, lumps and bumps, he treated them all. Infectious diseases were passed on to the Fever Hospital in Cork Street but he did all surgical cases himself, except for eyes. The parents brought them in, every bit as concerned and caring as parents today but, he considered, more thankful and unquestioning. 'My word was law,' he declared. He worked over one hundred hours a week without any income from his public patients. However, to keep the wolf from the door, he set up a private practice in Frederick Street, the Harley Street of Dublin's northside at the time.

Clearly, John Shanley broke new ground in every area of life. He claimed to have been one of the first in Dublin to use streptomycin in the treatment of tubercular meningitis. The patient in question was a young girl, gravely ill. He explained to the parents about this new drug and convinced them that if no further treatment was given, she would die. Following treatment, the girl recovered and went on to become a cellist, which gave him great satisfaction every time he saw her name on a concert programme. He also remembered the first time he operated on a young boy who had a general anaesthetic. 'I couldn't understand, I thought he had died, the abdomen was so quiet,' he revealed. Certainly, anaesthetics made life so much easier for the surgeon.

Medical politics was also making strides. The Irish branch of the British Medical Association (BMA) had been formed in 1864 and, having been appointed honorary secretary in 1924, Mr Shanley worked tirelessly towards achieving independence. When this finally came about in 1936 due to the sudden death of the medical secretary, he took over the post, also in an honorary capacity. He continued to be closely connected with this organisation, which became the Irish Medical Association in 1938, and he served two terms as its president.

The Second World War brought a new dimension to his already varied life. As chairman of the Irish Red Cross, he organised refugee centres for the many children arriving from both Britain and mainland Europe. Houses were appropriated, equipped and staffed. Indeed the Irish Red Cross was widely praised internationally for its work during these years. For the duration of the Emergency, Mr Shanley and two other surgeons – Mr MacAuley from the Mater and Mr Doolin from St Vincent's – were gazetted into the Irish Army as Hon. Majors. They underwent special training for all foreseeable contingencies, such as gas attacks, and prepared disaster plans for use in the event of mass casualties.

In the years following the war, Mr Shanley was as busy as ever. Mention his name then in any city household and there would always be someone who said, 'Of course, I knew him. He was wonderful to me/my brother/my daughter...' Medical politics continued to occupy him too. He served on many ministerial commissions and also as a member of the Medical Registration Council. An extremely humble man, he had many honours and distinctions bestowed on him, but he admitted to being especially proud of having been created a Knight of the Papal Order of St Gregory in 1973.

On the occasion of being made a Papal Knight, Mr John Shanley (right)
with Mr J. McAuliffe-Curtain (left) and Monsignor Cecil Barrett (centre) in 1973.

John Shanley left behind a lifetime of service to the State and to the children of Dublin. Truly, he lived up to his Gaelic name – Seán Laoch – the Old Warrior.

Mrs Joy Fitzgerald interviewed John Shanley in his home in Merrion Square in March 1989, when he was 94-years-old. He died at the ripe old age of 101.

RECORDS OF THE TIME

ÁINE M. O'LOUGHLIN

During my time in Temple Street, I was very impressed by the pleasant atmosphere and the friendly staff always willing to help. This was very obvious from the day I first came for interview in 1981. I have seen a lot of changes and improvements since then, all of which have enhanced the day-to-day running of the Hospital. Naturally, a lot of staff have come and gone too.

Firstly, I worked on wages for a brief period, spent some time in the X-ray Department, but was later appointed as medical supervisor/secretary in the typing pool (or Medical Secretariat). At that time two of us were working in the office, and we did the entire clinical correspondence, etc. for the consultants, who numbered about ten. (When I left they numbered at least forty.) We worked in a small prefab in the garden, where 'the grass was sometimes visible through the floorboards', and with a few other discrepancies in the 'woodwork here and there'. Numerous departments have since been formed, i.e. Orthopaedic, Neurology, Metabolic, Surgery, Plastic Surgery, Dermatology, ENT, and a Casualty consultant was also appointed. Prior to that, the queues took up a lot of 'space in the lane'. All these departments have secretaries/clerical officers now. Also some of the consultants were assigned a personnel secretary due to the large amount of patients attending the various clinics.

When I first came to the Hospital there was a staff of three in the Medical Records Department, but now there are over thirty. We worked on manual typewriters for some years, and then progressed to electric machines which were indeed gladly welcomed. When the whole hospital was computerised and we got our word processors, it made a fantastic improvement all round. In trying to locate a hospital number for patient's details, we had to previously wade through a card index that was very slow. These cards have all vanished now, and the computerised system is much faster and efficient. Around that time we also moved to the new Outpatients which allowed much more space.

One of the most extraordinary figures in the Hospital was Miss Butler, who was secretary/manager, personnel manager, part-time wages clerk, and accounts clerk at times. I never knew how she managed it all, but she always seemed to keep a 'cool head' and get there on target. On her retirement, a secretary/manager was appointed and later a Personnel Department established, which was a great asset to the Hospital. A Stores Department was opened up later on, while the Accounts Department and Wages Departments have enlarged considerably over the years.

On my retirement from Temple Street, I was happy, as I had a pleasant time there and endeavoured to do my work to the best of my ability. Naturally being 'human' and working with 'individuals' did mean we had our 'ups and downs', occasionally. I may even have had 'mild' or 'stormy' discussions with some consultants who were sometimes reluctant to do discharge summaries, etc. on a regular basis. However, they never escaped! My final wish is that when the Hospital moves to the Mater Campus that it will have the same pleasant, friendly and efficient atmosphere.

Ms Áine M. O'Loughlin is a former staff member of the Medical Records Department.

CEREBRAL STAR

NEIL O'DOHERTY (1928-1999)

PROF DENIS GILL

Ample Buck Mulligan ambled from Eccles Street toward the Temple theatre of divinity and doctoring where he encountered the professor of paediatric muttering and misericording that the incarcerated inhospitables of that erstwhile institution could no longer be confined to their cots and chamber beds to teach his mendicant students but preferred their own scholarly leisure and learnings and electricals in the tuition and recreation ante chambers distant from the doctors and their daily deliberations; to which musings Mulligan replied, 'Quod erat demonstrandurn, if pedes iatrix means foot doctor, then the children are voting with their feet'.

'Can one really believe that it took the doctors one hundred years to realise that what the children of Ireland need is not more medication but rather more education?'

Those imaginary Joycean rambles and Shavian grumble might well have come from the pen of the late Neil O'Doherty, who liked not only Joyce and Shaw and Brinsley Sheridan, but also Kubrick, Jacques Tati, *Private Eye* (especially the Colemanballs column to which he occasionally and surreptitiously contributed), Dorothy Parker and a myriad more.

Neil was a polymath, a gourmand, a filmbuff, an intrepid traveller, a composer of anagrams, amalgams and a collector of anecdotes. A man of words and wisdom. He used to say of one colleague with whom he had perennial disagreements that they were in 'an antlers locked situation'. On my first trip to the Middle East he advised me to bring with me some rubber bands, two toilet rolls, and a golf ball – 'Work it out, son.'

Neil is missed for his formidable intellect, his idiosyncratic, quirky dry humour, and his amiable eccentricities. He devoured books, photographed prodigiously, and collected an enormous number of clinical, teaching and 'funny' slides. The O'Doherty Slide Archive rests outside my office as a tribute to his energy, observational ability and interest in his patients. The filing system was locked in Neil's memory!

Neil's inquisitive and enquiring nature stimulated him to consult widely. Many of his former registrars will recall, with mixed frustration and fondness, his orders during rounds or in the Outpatients: 'Ring Menkes now', 'Get me McCusick', 'Call my friend Bob Gorlin, he'll have the answer', 'Where's Smith?', 'Consult the Baraister database.' Neil maintained a lifelong interest in dysmorphology coupled with great sympathy and mustered support for the affected families.

The internet unfortunately came too late for Neil: he would have loved it! He brought back to Ireland his skills and experiences learned with *the* developmental dame, Mary Sheridan. He published a photographic text on the Battered Child with 'guaranteed Irish illustrations' and highlighted child abuse in this Republic. Published in 1979, his work entitled *The Atlas of the Newborn* was a source of great pride to him and was, in its time, unique. His text 'Inspecting the Newborn Baby's Eyes' contained many extraordinary observations, illustrations, and practice points. He also contributed a text on the neurological examination of the newborn.

Neil Justin O'Doherty was a member of the historical O'Doherty clan of Inishowen whose history dates back to the 15th century. Neil, however, spent much of his life in Dublin and lived in 'Sunnybank', a gorgeous Georgian house on the banks of the Liffey, and a former residence of Lord Northcliffe. Indeed the house features in *Finnegan's Wake*. He received his secondary and medical school education in Dublin, graduating in 1952. He then obtained his MD, MRCP, MRCPI, followed in 1958 by DCH! He did house jobs in Dublin, London (Whipps Cross, Whittington, and London Chest) and an SHO post in Dr Steeven's Hospital. He commenced paediatric training in 1956 in the Evelina, followed by Great Ormond Street and Queen Charlotte's. He did a registrar post in Newcastle and then crossed to North America where as a research fellow he worked in Sick Children's Toronto, and then Johns Hopkins. In 1962 he returned to Guy's Hospital where he served as senior paediatric registrar and senior lecturer until 1967. Prior to returning to Dublin as consultant paediatrician, he had been appointed to the West Middlesex.

In Dublin he served The Children's Hospital Temple Street, St Michael's House – the handicapped child community of North Dublin – and taught the students of University College Dublin where he was associate professor.

I'll wager that Neil left his hallmark at all of these institutions and was remembered long after his departure by head porters, hospital photographers, library curators, administrators ('always to be given short shrift') and ward sisters, as a man of distinction, as a mincer of words, a character of eccentric wit, accumulated wisdom, remarkable memory, cyclothymic humour, combative disposition.

Neil always turned up to the BPA at York. He contributed to CESP. He cared. He is missed by his five sisters, by his admiring colleagues, by his patients, many of whom kept in touch long after his retirement. 'The Doc', as Neil was affectionately known, has long been recounted and recalled in stories and anecdotes.

O'Doherty was a star, often shining brilliantly, occasionally shooting in the wrong direction, always illuminating, whose lines will continue to light up our lives. A wandering star. An idiosyncratic star. A cerebral star.

Prof Denis Gill is Professor of Paediatric Medicine at The Children's Hospital.

NO REGRETS

AILEEN NOONAN

My time at The Children's Hospital, Temple Street began in 1960. I was interviewed – which was somewhat informal – by the radiologist, Dr Richard Reynolds. In fact, I was advised to apply for the post by another radiologist, Dr Michael Magan, with whom I had worked as radiographer in Dublin Corporation. Dr Magan was a nephew of the then Mother Rectress, Mother Baptist. So in those days it was 'who you knew!' It was indeed complimentary to be recommended and in fairness to myself, I was offered a post in a major hospital at the same time, and chose Temple Street because of its known friendliness, and of course, for the opportunity to help sick children. *I never had any regrets.*

When I joined the Temple Street there was one other radiographer, Cepta Bell. I replaced the late Maureen Claffey. We gave a 24-hour service, which meant that one of us was 'on call' every second night and weekend. There was no such thing as bleeps or mobile phones, and owning a car was unaffordable in the early days of my career. So, the only way to travel in and out, while on call, was by bus. If you were called after 'last bus', the hospital sent a taxi to collect you. We often went to the cinema while on call. We would leave our name at the cinema desk and tell the usherette where we were sitting. This was common practice among radiographers. So no matter where you went, it was necessary to be at the other end of a telephone. During those days we were paid, approximately 47 cent (in today's money) for a 'call out', even though you might X-ray five patients, and we were not paid for transport before midnight. Our weekly salary was approximately £7.00 (€8.80), which was delivered to us in a brown envelope by Miss Butler, the hospital secretary. Brown envelopes have a different meaning today!! Miss Butler, busily *h'mm'd* herself through the day. She was also the hospital accountant, recruitment officer, personnel officer, problem solver – you name it, she did it! When she retired, she was replaced by approximately ten people!

Miss Elizabeth Butler.

During those earlier years the X-ray Department was situated in what is now the ICU – in fact half that size. It consisted of a fair-sized X-ray room, a tiny radiologist's office and a darkroom. In the radiologist's office there was a ladder leading to a loft, where all films were filed. There was a cabinet in the X-ray room for filing the more recent films. The X-ray equipment was adequate except for our one and only portable machine. It was constantly going out of order! Before moving it from one area of the Hospital to the other, it was necessary to take it apart and reassemble it before use. The same portable machine served the Theatre. I remember on one occasion while the portable machine was out of order that Mr MacAuley, the orthopaedic surgeon, successfully reduced five fractures in our X-ray room. He was, of course, assisted by an anaesthetist and theatre staff. I think we got a new machine after that!

Patients for X-ray waited on the stairs (where ICU visitors wait today). All trolley and wheelchair cases came up on the lift and made their way through Surgical Flat and waited outside the door, which was also beside the entrance to Theatre. It certainly was not the most ideal arrangement.

During those early years of my employment, there was no ramp between Casualty Department/St Michael's Ward and the main hospital. So all babies for X-ray, or Theatre, had to come across the garden in hail, rain, or snow! I think the ramp was built in the mid-sixties, and as you can imagine, was a welcome improvement.

A lot of activity took place in the darkroom. Films were developed manually in a wet processing tank. It took fifteen minutes to develop an X-ray film for wet viewing, and four to five hours to wash and dry, before it was ready for official reading. X-ray films now take forty-five seconds to process – which is still not short enough for some people today! We did not have automatic processing until we moved to the present location in the early seventies. From a radiographer's point of view, this advancement in technology was hugely appreciated – no more making up gallons of chemicals, and no more discolouration underneath fingernails from developer solutions.

Despite the drudgery, the darkroom was a great social centre – staff constantly coming and going to view their patient's films. We made our 'elevenses' in the darkroom, where the physios joined us. Sr Joseph Claude (from St Patrick's Ward) visited us daily. She loved a read of *The Irish Times* and a chat. She was also into matchmaking but sadly failed with me! Sr Mary Arsenius was also a constant visitor but was a lot friendlier with my predecessors, especially Maureen Claffey. Despite the fact that I joined Temple Street because of its friendliness, I was probably less friendly myself than most people, mainly because of shyness, so I may have given the wrong impression many a time when dealing with Hospital staff.

Getting back to the X-ray Department, all barium studies were done in pitch darkness. Much explaining had to be done to the child and carer before the procedure took place. It must have been quite traumatic for the little children. All of that was normal at the time and today screening studies take place in the daylight, thanks again to modern technology. The telephone for the X-ray Department was outside the door, which was also shared by Theatre and Surgical Flat. There was certainly a lot of time spent answering calls for each other!

Following Mother Baptist's time as Rectress, there was Mother Canisius. Mother C went shopping every Christmas to Switzers on Grafton Street, and bought generous presents for all the staff in the Hospital. I remember getting very glamorous nighties!

It was not until Sr Ann Eucharia was appointed Mother Rectress that we got a staff canteen. The first day it opened, Sr Ann E was in the garden saying her prayers, and with one eye on the canteen she noticed a very long large queue waiting for lunch. She had bought a limited amount of crockery and cutlery and felt very nervous about the outcome. She was praying that everything would go okay – it did! The canteen was a welcome addition. Before that, it was necessary to go downtown for a bite to eat. In those days, there was no such thing as pub grub. Even if you brought sandwiches in with you, there was no area in the hospital where you could make a cup of tea and eat lunch. And if you were on 24-hour duty, you could not depend on getting a meal at home. Apart from satisfying your stomach, the canteen was a welcome social area. It did help you to get to know people from other departments. Before I retired, I used to enjoy having my breakfast there with other early-morning-to-work travellers.

Eventually we moved to our new Department in 1972. To us, this was like a five-star hotel, *webbed space*. We now had two X-ray rooms, and even had a staffroom where we could change into our uniforms and make a cup of tea. The Department was also conveniently situated near to Outpatient and Casualty Departments, from where most of our little clients came. But, again as time went on, we just got busier and busier. As a result, our complement of radiographers and secretarial staff was increased. Dr Joan MacCarthy, our radiologist, also got much needed help. It was at this stage that Dr Veronica Donoghue joined the team and that the Ultrasound and Nuclear Medicine Departments were opened.

Parents and children certainly became more knowledgeable in regard to procedures and radiation. A child would have the X-ray protective apron on him or her before you'd have time to say 'hello'. On one occasion a stressed-out mother losing her patience had great difficulty in holding a child still for X-ray. Despite encouraging words by me from the control area, the mother said, 'Look here, you hold the child and I'll press the button.'

Temple Street opened its doors 130 years ago, I was there for forty of those years – almost one third of its existence. I feel very proud of that. I would like to pay tribute to the Irish Sisters of Charity, and their staff, who over all those years devoted themselves to the care of sick children and their needs. Long live The Children's Hospital – a hospital which, I know, is well loved by the people of North Dublin.

Aileen Noonan was Radiographer at The Children's Hospital from 1960 to 2000.

TWENTY–SEVEN HAPPY YEARS

MR SEAMUS O'RIAIN

I was appointed as consultant plastic surgeon at Temple Street on 20 March 1968 and was to spend twenty-seven very happy years there until my retirement in 1995. Having trained in the NHS for eight years, the latter four being in major plastic surgery units, the 'set-up' in Temple Street appeared very small at first. We operated in twin theatres where facilities and equipment were basic. There was a third operating theatre, which was a continuing source of discussion as to whether it could be opened or not – it never was up to the time that the new theatres opened and we had a three-theatre suite.

My first impressions were the excellent standard of the work being carried out in this small hospital. The co-operation of all the staff and the expertise, especially of the nursing staff on the wards, was impressive. The training programme for nurses in Temple Street was second to none and this, coupled with the commitment of the Sisters and nurses on the wards, produced a most reassuring working environment for a surgeon.

There had been an excellent tradition of work on cleft lip and palates in Temple Street and my training in the UK was directed principally to gaining knowledge of how to treat these patients. Some years after my appointment, I realised that William Doolin, who was the senior surgeon in St Vincent's Hospital, had also worked at Temple Street in the 1930s and 1940s. He had done excellent work there and produced a superb account of operating on two hundred children with cleft lip and palates that was published, if my memory serves me well, in the *Irish Journal of Medical Sciences* around 1947. The results as published in his usual self-critical way were very good, but the most remarkable aspect was the extremely low operative mortality rate which would compare favourably with any similar account at that time. It is perhaps worth noting that William Doolin took himself off to Paris to study the treatment of cleft lip and palate with Victor

Veau, who was a leading authority in this field at the time. Mr Doolin also had a correspondence with Harold Gillies in later years, and the latter sent him a copy of one of his textbooks.

In 1968 John Shanley was the dominant figure in the Hospital; senior surgeon, chairman of the Board, and so on. Despite his advanced years, he was a very effective operative surgeon and had a reputation for expertise in carrying out Ramstdets operation on infants with pyloric stenosis. To watch him carrying out one of these operations was an experience in expertise and time saving!

Over the twenty-seven years that I worked in Temple Street, there were many developments and advances despite the perennial problem of lack of funds. These advances could have been so much faster and greater if the bedevilling attitude and suspicion of the two major children's hospitals for each other did not persist year in, year out, *ad infinitum.* Whenever the prospect of both institutions developing a specialty at one site was mooted, despite a share of goodwill on both sides and pleas including offers of funding from the National Advisory bodies, there developed a retreat to the trenches. Both sides squared up eyeball to eyeball, the time-dishonoured attitude prevailed – 'not an inch'.

It is reassuring that at the end of the day the Hospital will be relocated on the Mater Hospital Campus which can only be a good thing for the development of paediatric services in Dublin and Ireland.

Mr Seamus O'Riain was Consultant Plastic Surgeon at The Children's Hospital from 1968 to 1995.

MAINTAINING THE HOUSE

JACK BROGAN

My earliest memory of Temple Street goes back to 1935 when, as a young boy, I was admitted to St Bridget's Ward for a tonsillectomy. I remember the journey from the ward along what, I later learned, was called the 'Tonsil Corridor' to a small operating theatre located in the Outpatients Department. When I had returned to the ward and was recovering from the operation, I have vivid memories of being 'asked' to take a mug of unsweetened lemon juice, which I had great difficulty in doing.

Four years later, just before Christmas, I had a cycling accident that resulted in an injury to my leg. My uncle, Tom Keogh, took me to see Mr John Shanley, who examined me in the front parlour, now the board room. He decided that a surgical procedure was required to correct the situation. I was admitted the following day to Surgical Flat and remained in hospital for two weeks. Until recently, I had a photograph that appeared in the *Irish Press* of me sitting up in bed watching the nurses preparing the ward for Christmas. Little did I think that eight short years later, I would be helping to decorate the same ward and would be involved in decorating the hospital at Christmas for the next fifty years.

My uncle had been providing electrical services to the hospital from 1922. When I started to serve my apprenticeship with him in 1947, the reliance on electrical equipment was not as critical as in modern times, consequently the electrical services were provided on a 'call out' basis. The supervisors of our work were the Reverend Mother or Sister Ministress at the time. You then submitted an invoice for works carried out to Lily Butler for payment. This invoice was put amongst all the others on her very large desk, and on occasions you would be told, 'I can't pay this, I have no money.'

You would accept this statement knowing, however, that when monies became available the account would be settled.

During the fifty-one years I worked with the Hospital, it was constantly changing and expanding to cope with the demands placed on it by the evolving nature of medical and surgical procedures. The first of these changes was the purchase of No. 9 Temple Street and its conversion from a tenement building to a home for additional domestic and nursing staff that had been employed. This took place in 1947/48. Then in 1950 the third floor was added to St Michael's Block and called St Michael's B. The Laboratory, which had been housed in the Outpatients Department, roughly where the Pharmacy is today, was built over the Mortuary.

The heating and hot water services for the whole Hospital were supplied from a large boiler house with eight small boilers located at various points throughout the buildings. All of these boilers were coal-fired, and had to be attended to seven days a week. During the winter months, fires had to be lit in all the wards to maintain some heat in the buildings. This meant that coal had to be brought to all the wards in the evening and the fires cleaned out every morning and set for the evening light-up. In 1954, it was decided to install an oil-fired boiler to serve the main building, operating theatres and laundry. Then over the following years, all other coal-fired boilers were dispensed with and all systems linked to the main boiler. This made life so much easier for the staff involved and heating services were then maintained on a 24-hour basis. The cost of running the new boiler at that time was about 78 cent per hour (in today's money), which was a considerable saving on the coal-fired system that it replaced.

In the mid-fifties the houses to the left of the Hospital were demolished and a new nurses home was built, known as St Joan's. This building consisted of sleeping quarters on three floors, an extension to the convent on the top floor, nurses' sitting rooms and the Matron's living quarters and office on the ground floor. The dining area for nurses and medical staff was located in the lower floor level.

The sixties saw further development with the purchase of Nos. 1–8 Temple Street. When all the tenants had been rehoused, these buildings were demolished, and in the late sixties work commenced on the building of St Mary's Nurses Home. The Assembly Hall was built around 1961 and great use made of it in its early days by running nurses dances and sales of work. Indeed both functions were always well supported. Later on, it was used for day-long conferences and as a medical student lecture area. I remember it best for the Christmas pantomime, which was run for so many years with considerable enjoyment and success.

Because the Hospital was expanding and additional electrical equipment was being installed, it was apparent that the electrical supplies were unable to cope with the new demands being placed on them. As a result, it was decided that a major upgrading was required. I started this work in 1963 and it took about eighteen months to complete. During the mid-sixties it was decided to build St Frances' Clinic at the end of the Casualty lane. To accomplish this, a farrier's workshop had to be demolished. Up until then, this was where two local bakeries – Johnston Mooney & O'Brien, and Kennedy's (both of whom delivered their bread in horse-drawn vehicles) – took their horses to be shod. As this means of transport was being replaced by motor vehicles, the farrier's business was then in decline. Today the forecourt of St Frances' Clinic is roughly on the site of this forge.

During the last thirty years there have been many developments to upgrade and improve services within the Hospital; new wards, units, clinics, theatres, and departments were established and existing ones extended. Other changes which took place during my fifty-one years with the Hospital included the replacement of telephonic equipment (twice), the replacement of the front lift and the conversion of the oil burner to a gas-fired unit. The laundry was converted from what was a labour intensive to a semi-automatic facility, and piped medical gases were installed to replace the trolley-mounted cylinders. The installation of the fire alarm systems was great fun with lots of false alarms and 'discussions' with very irate fire officers at times. The list of changes goes on and on, but space does not permit me to expand on all of these.

You might be forgiven for thinking that it was work, work, work, during all these years but there was a wonderful social side to my time with the Hospital. For instance, there were the visits to the 'stress free' zone of the hospital – Sheary's, now The Temple Bar – where the lads would gather for a light refreshment sometimes to be joined by the lassies. The nurses dances, which I referred to earlier, led in time to the enjoyable annual dress dances. These were held in what is now Jury's Hotel in Ballsbridge. I was only a spectator at the inter-hospital soccer and hockey competitions, but participated in the tennis tournaments, which were also great fun. There were also birthday parties, marriages, staff retirement parties, the Hospital Centenary celebrations (a weeklong affair!). And lots of other functions that I thoroughly enjoyed. But above all else, the memory of the wonderful people I met and worked with, over all of this time, will always be with me.

I feel very proud and privileged of my uncle's involvement from 1922, and my association from 1947, with all of changes over the years. Finally, I wish all involved in the further development of this wonderful institution every success in their endeavours.

Jack Brogan was Maintenance Supervisor at The Children's Hospital, and retired in 1998 after 51 years of service.

The infamous hospital boilers with Jack Kennerk, maintenance supervisor, and Willie Malone, plumber (below).

ASPECTS OF SURGERY

Mr Edward J. Guiney

On 9 January 1967 I received a letter from Mother Teresa Anthony, Superior General of the Sisters of Charity appointing me as assistant paediatric surgeon to The Children's Hospital, Temple Street. When I joined the staff, the now legendary Mother Canisius was Reverend Mother.

The general surgical staff consisted of John Shanley, who although retired from clinical practice, continued to attend daily at the Hospital and to play a very active advisory role regarding its activities. Mr Kevin Maughan and Mr James O'Neill were also general surgeons while Mr Sean Lavan (who represented Ireland as an athlete at the 1924 and 1928 Olympic Games) attended as surgeon to the Outpatients. Mr Frank Duff was urological surgeon, Mr Fergus Donovan was neurosurgeon and Mr Seamus O'Riain was plastic surgeon. Mr D. Donoghue and Dr Catherine Fitzpatrick were the eye surgeons, while Mr MacAuliffe-Curtin and Mr George Fennell were in charge of the ENT Department. In addition, Mr P. MacAuley supervised a very active Orthopaedic Department. Drs Ned Gumbrielle, Evelyn Gallagher and Winnie Tempany were the anaesthetists.

From the above it is apparent that the Hospital had a highly skilled and specialised surgical service. I retired in 1996 having spent twenty-nine years on the staff during which time the hospital underwent extraordinary development in keeping with the technical, sociological and therapeutic advances of the past three decades.

This evolution of the Hospital was manifested in many ways. Initially, it was seen in the construction of the Assembly/Lecture Hall which has been a focal point of activities for many years. In this regard, the incorporation of St George's Hall in recent years has been a major boon for the teaching and academic facilities at the Hospital. In a relatively short few years, new Radiology and Pathology Departments were constructed and commissioned; the directors being Dr Joan McCarthy and Dr Seamus Cahalane, respectively. The comprehensive services which these two Departments provided were the essential complement to the ever-increasing challenges which the Surgery and Anaesthetics Departments had to rise to during the 1980s and 1990s – as we know, it was a period of economic cutbacks that were dreadfully frustrating and from which we are still striving to recover.

Nevertheless, despite the prevailing mood, the Hospital secured agreement from the Department of Health and pushed ahead with the construction of a new Operating Suite and Intensive Care Unit. It cannot be overemphasised how important this development was for the future viability and continuing morale of the Hospital. The inclusion within the ICU of facilities for the support and management of the critically ill neonate was pivotal and symbolic of the Hospital's standing and expertise. The success of this highly skilled arm of ICU was in no small part due to the advent of anaesthetist, Dr Declan Warde, and specialist neonatologists such as Prof Thomas Clarke, Prof Thomas Mathews, Dr John Murphy and Dr Ann Twomey to the consultant staff of the Hospital.

In the light of the financial constraints being placed on hospitals and in response to the changing attitude to the admission of children, the establishment of Day Wards was inevitable. The Day Unit, the A & E Department and the Outpatients are the busiest sections of the Hospital. Certainly, Dr Peter Keenan's appointment was another beacon.

Thinking back over the past thirty years or so, it brings to mind certain individuals whose involvement in the Hospital was particularly special. All who knew her will recall the 'original mould' of secretary managers, Miss Elizabeth Butler, with affection. Dan Kelly, Ray FitzGerald, Prem Puri and Fergal Quinn are close associates who have not only made a major contribution to Temple Street, but to paediatric surgery in the Republic. I would ask others, who have been very busy on behalf of Temple Street's children, to please forgive your omission here on the basis of my fallibility and in the interests of brevity.

There are, however, a few others whom I will never forget. Sr M. Arsenius of Top Flat, who gave me such support one night and early morning during a fatal clinical problem. Also Sr Ann Eucharia, WARD SISTER, MATRON and RECTRESS in sequence, and gentle Sr Olive of Michael's B. These and many others of the Community were responsible for that special *grá* or indefinable *caritas* that permeated the hospital in my time and, of which, I was privileged to be part.

Mr Edward J. Guiney was Consultant Paediatric Surgeon at The Children's Hospital, and retired in 1996 after 29 years of service.

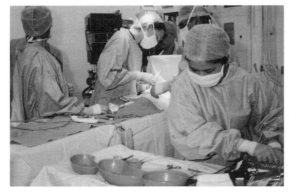

Theatre staff at work in Theatre 3.

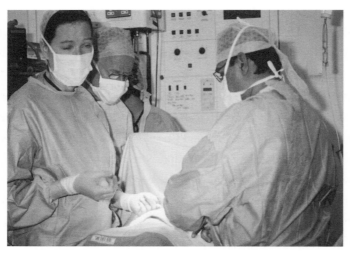

(Left to right) surgeons Ms Sinéad Hassett, Prof Raymond Fitzgerald and Mr Muhammad Choudry.

A TIME FOR LAUGHTER,
A TIME FOR TEARS

STATIA BRENNAN MELLON

In September 1967, I started nursing in Temple Street Hospital. I was so lonely and lost but within a few days I made what were to be friends for life. My class was very special. Indeed Miss Murphy, the Home Sister, used to say that we were the best group she ever had. She was such a lovely woman, who would take no nonsense but was still very kind.

The head porter, Paddy Doyle, was also so special. My memories of Paddy are all good, full of fun, so generous and helpful. He cried like a baby the day I left Temple Street. His tears touched me greatly because PADDY *WAS* TEMPLE STREET.

Then there were the tutors – Sr Joseph Cyril was such a great one. She had the greatest ability to impart knowledge to her students. Mrs Corrigan, Ms McHale and Mrs Nagle – they too were all great. For all the time I spent at Temple Street, I was lucky that Sr Ann Eucharia was there too. She was marvellous and communicated so well with her staff. There was a lovely natural, laid-back way about her. A great person to get things done, she was so competent, but still had a great sense of fun about her.

Luckily, I moved through my training fairly well without much trouble, only meeting a cross Sister or staff nurse here and there. Certainly, as one gets on in one's career, one realises that nursing is highly responsible and no easy job.

Sr Teresa Eucharia was my first Sister-in-Charge. I didn't know at that time that I was going to spend most of my career, after completing my general training and midwifery, with her in Casualty. She was the most wonderful woman I have ever met in my life. The type of woman you felt so lucky to have known. She was so kind and caring and taught me so much. Having developed a great rapport with the poor children, she looked at every aspect of their lives, especially their pastoral care. Everything about her was so fair, so conscientious, so kind, so funny, so unselfish. She gave every ounce of her energy to her staff and patients. None of the staff left Casualty for years – all because of Sr Teresa Eucharia. I will never forget her.

We all had fantastic fun in Casualty. The children and their parents were beautiful people. They were so direct and, of course, I loved the Dublin accent and how they would express things. We laughed so much, it was so good. I wish I could bring it all back again. In those days, there was so much poverty and sadness in the inner city. Somehow, these people battled against all the odds. I was humbled by them, especially the women. They seemed to be able to look after their children so well, despite all their own difficulties. For many families, the father was not around. That must have been particularly difficult. The children were often craving for a little bit of attention. I hope I made a difference for some of these fine children along the way.

The people I remember with great fondness, apart from those whom I have mentioned already, include Sr M. Arsenius, the late Sr Thomas Moore, Ms Phillips in CCU, the late Rita King, Bridie Carroll in St Philomena's, the carpenter Tommy Shields, Dr Cahalane, Dr Peter Keenan, and all the X-ray and Laboratory staff. Ina Curley in St Patrick's Ward taught me so much, especially how to give my first injection. The kitchen staff and cleaners were marvellous, but too many to mention. However, one woman in particular was very kind to me. Her name was Mrs Reddy and she worked in St Brigid's Ward so that she could put her family through college. She was great for keeping us out of trouble! Memorable too are the staff on the switchboard – Mrs Finn, Mary and Valerie. And as for the fun we had with Adele O'Connor and Carmel in Admissions!

I would like to take this opportunity to thank all the staff in Temple Street for making my time there so enjoyable. It is a very special place. Hats off to all the doctors who worked there over the years and, of course, all the nurses, especially my wonderful colleagues in Casualty. Thanks also to all the Sisters of Charity I have met along the way – what wonderful people, so dedicated. I have been so lucky.

Statia Brennan Mellon is a former Staff Nurse at The Children's Hospital.

MATERIA POETICA

MR GEORGE FENNELL

THE NEW XANADU

(with deepest apologies to S.T. Coleridge)

At Sunnybank did Kubla Khan a stately pleasure house decree
Close by where Anna Livia ran
By fields and wretched autobahn
Down to the Ringsend sea.

Among his lawns the great Khan sat in sad and contemplative mood
And looked upon the World with pain
Saying to himself again
"What do I see that's good?"

His mind grows dim, his thoughts are wild
And in a faery voice he sings
Of long dead days and other things
When he was but a child.

With Northcliffe, Joyce and Oscar Wilde and loony Beckett he doth speak,
He mutters words of long-dead men
With imprecations now and then
As he the truth doth seek.

How often did he take and mould the shaping of an infant hand
Which, trembling, pointed to the sky

Accompanied with plaintive cry
"Is this, then, the Promised Land?"

Erect a plaque high up the wall, engraved in words of glittering gold!
"Here lived the finest of them all
Professor, sage, and, over all
One whose words were bold!"

"So when the last and dreadful hour this crumbling pageant shall devour
The trumpet shall be heard on high,
The dead shall live, the living die,
And music shall untune the sky."

For Prof O'D, Prof of Growth & Development, who lived at 'Sunnybank', Chapelizod.

THE NOSE

The nose on your face is a wonderful place
And its functions take much in the telling;
Its shape may be moulded by region or race,
And it's not just for sniffing and smelling.

It's useful for picking, or cocking a snook,
It wrinkles in doubt or disdain,
You can bury it deep in the leaves of a book –
It derives from the front of your brain.

It is button or Roman, or Grecian, or snub,
Long, short, straight, crooked or bent;
The Eskimo's fun, when fishing is done, is to rub
It, when mating, in igloo or tent.
It can wriggle or poke, or be put out of joint,

Or stuck into anyone's business;
It can look like a joke and quite disappoint;
It measures degrees of Strabismus.

It reddens with drink, turns blue with the cold,
It's cut off for punitive reasons;
It presages rain, can run like a drain,
And it opens and shuts with the Seasons.

Cyrano's protruded and made quite a noise
And hindered access to his lips;
If Helen of Troy's had been big, like a boy's,
She could never have launched all those ships.
Parson has one (although in a rude place),
A clown's large and red as a rule;
A snob can look down it and make you lose face
And feel you're no end of a fool.

It drains off your tears
In colds it blocks up with catarrh;
If its veins are engorged as you pass through the years
People know you're inclined to a 'jar'.

If you treasure this paragon (although, like a friend,
It oft comes between husband and wife)
It will lead you along 'til you come to the end
And stick close to you all through your life.

THE PROFESSOR'S DREAM

Among the rumpled sheets he lay,
His brow was moist with sweat
As he saw in tortured dreams of day
The little children he had met.

Some had one nose, some had two,
Twelve fingers here, an extra toe,
One eye green, the other blue,
And strange things grew down there below.

The visions rained down like confetti,
Klippel-Feil, Hallevorden-Spatz,
Haufmann-Strauss and Franceschetti,
Tails like dogs and heads like cats.

Hand-Schüller-Christian, Marfan, Downes,
Laughing at his disarray,
Danced 'round his bed like little clowns,
Driving reason far away.

They brought him one to calm his slumbers,
An ear each side his little head,
Ten fingers, toes of normal number,
A central nose, gold hair on head.

A brow as fine as Coriolanus,
A torso of proportioned size,
Two testicles, a patent anus,
Shapely head and clear blue eyes.
"Oh, what is this and what is here?"
He muttered names of long dead men,

And he crossed himself for fear,
We said "he'll ne'er be sane again".

"Sturge-Weber, Waardenburg," he cried,
"Come to aid me in my pain,
This vision strange at my bed-side
Never let me see again!"

Our little jest had gone askew
(Oh, listen to his strange wild scream!)
We never should have let him view
An entirely normal human being!

For Neil O'Doherty, Prof of Growth & Development, Temple Street

THE MERCHANT

When I pass on, what shall the verdict be? –
That in that body lived a man who tried
But failed, was given eyes to see
The beauty all around, but died

Before he relished all the treasures cast
Within his reach; whose reason
Should have smiled when skies o'ercast
Brought in the Winter season,

When soon warm Summer followed Spring,
And then the golden leaves began to fall;
Thus Earth did Nature's praises sing –
But I ignored it all.
The foolish searching for material gain

Obscured much music, love and art;
The Poet bared his soul in vain,
I set my lonely self apart.

Sometimes I looked up to the sky,
Saw only assets bought or sold.
No use now to wish and sigh,
My grave will not be lined with gold.

Could that strange tale of long ago,
Of broken bread and Holy Grail,
Have some relevance here below,
Might His promises prevail?
Let's close the ledgers now and shut the till,
And walk towards that vague Promised Land
Where souls awake when hearts are still –
Rich man and pauper, hand in hand.

RESURRECTION

The still, dark cloud of death hangs quiet
Upon Jerusalem, all is night.
A thousand suns bear not the power
To light one fragment of this hour
Of degradation, fear and lies.

Prostrate on the hill above
Lies all the glory, hope and love.
Maternal anguish cries aloud,
Consigns humanity to the shroud
With tender helping hands and sighs.

The rumble of the closing tomb
Resembles not the sound of doom
To prisoners who cannot see
The open gates, for are not we
The gaolers of our soul?

But on the road to Emmaus shines
The light of lights, the dark confines
Of prison-house are shattered wide
For love and justice, side by side,
To enter and console.

Then, sounding on the Easter morn,
The happy voice of mankind borne
Upon the wings of freedom sings
A greeting to the King of kings,
"The Son of man again is born."

'Prize Poem', *The Cork Examiner,* 1950

Mr George Fennell is a former ENT Surgeon at The Children's Hospital.

NOTHING INSURMOUNTABLE

SR BERNADETTE MARY DUFFY, RSC

In the autumn of 1992 I was appointed to The Children's Hospital to replace Sr Ann Eucharia. More than twenty-five years had elapsed since my training days there. While many things had changed during those years, the important aspects of our ethos was highlighted and strengthened by our Mission Effectiveness Programme.

On arrival I was happy to see some familiar faces, but I realised there were many more whom I would get to know over the years. A happy atmosphere had always prevailed in the Hospital and was still flourishing.

The Hospital authorities were always very conscious of space restrictions and this was very evident to me when I arrived. At the end of my seven years with the help and co-operation of the Development Team, with continuous and successful fundraising and the benefit of donations received, improvement in some areas became evident in the upgrading of facilities to provide enhanced patient care. Needless to remark, there were inevitable difficulties to be faced, but because of loyal enthusiasm, the professional commitment and support of all members of staff nothing was insurmountable.

One of my great joys was to see that the spirit of Mary Aikenhead was alive and well in the Hospital and that our commitment to the disadvantaged was still very much our priority. The quality of care to which Mary Aikenhead aspired continued to be seen in the development of expertise at every level of patient care. I was very pleased to see the Mission Effectiveness Programme launched and this will provide long-term support for the continued well-being of the whole Hospital population.

As I left Temple Street in the Jubilee Year, I was very aware that the new millennium was also signalling a new phase in the life of The Children's Hospital. My good wishes go with all those who have the task of realising the plans that will provide the children of Dublin and the rest of Ireland with the services that will meet ALL of their needs, in a way that is inspired by our core values.

Sr Bernadette Mary Duffy, RSC is a former Sister Superior of the Religious Sisters of Charity.

Members of staff of different nationalities during Multicultural Awareness Week, November 2001.

HIPS AND BONES

PROF TIM O'BRIEN

In January 1980, I arrived at The Children's Hospital, Temple Street as the first full-time orthopaedic registrar. The intimate nature of the Hospital was immediately reinforced by a surprise visit from Miss Butler welcoming me to the institution. One got the immediate impression that everybody knew every other member of staff and that this closeness amongst staff was also reflected in one's attitude to patients. The impression was further reinforced at the Orthopaedic Outpatient Department, where the leg of the patient's chair was strapped to the consultation desk. This arrangement encouraged the patients at the clinic to remain in close proximity to the examiner and proved to be most effective. At that time, there were still tenements in the North Inner City and osteomyelitis was still a relatively common problem. The results of our treatment of osteomyelitis led to the publication of a seminal article entitled, 'The treatment of acute haematogenous osteomyelitis' in the *Journal of Bone and Joint Surgery* in 1982.

My interest in paediatric orthopaedic surgery thus stimulated, I sought a Fellowship at the Hospital for Sick Children in Toronto, with Prof R.B. Salter. His expertise in the management of hip dysplasia was unique, and he had developed the procedure of iliac osteotomy that cured acetabular dysplasia, a main component of hip dislocation. There followed a year in The Children's Hospital, Boston with Prof John E. Hall, the renowned scoliosis surgeon. On my return to Ireland, I was appointed as consultant orthopaedic surgeon to The Children's Hospital. It was one of the highlights of my career to welcome both Prof Salter and Prof Hall to the Hospital. Indeed, Prof Salter gave a demonstration of the iliac osteotomy, now known as the Salter osteotomy, on his visit. Subsequently, I produced a teaching video library version of the Salter osteotomy for the British Orthopaedic Association.

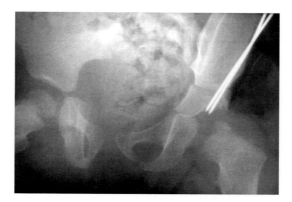

X-ray showing a Salter osteotomy.

I was appointed to the Abraham Colles Chair of Orthopaedic Surgery at the Royal College of Surgeons in Ireland in 1991, and maintained a keen interest in hip dysplasia. In 1996, I published my experience of the treatment of hip dysplasia at The Children's Hospital, Temple Street in a book entitled *Idiopathic Hip Dysplasia*. Other notable additions to the orthopaedic literature from Temple Street include the association between our climate and paediatric injuries published in the medical journal *Injury* in 1993. In addition, the term 'scutting' was introduced into the orthopaedic literature in 1989 also following its publication in *Injury*.

Prof Tim O'Brien was Professor of Orthopaedics at The Children's Hospital and retired in 1998.

'EVERYONE IS SO KIND'

SR THERESE CULHANE, RSC

It was late one night when I was coming off duty. I was very tired. Around a corner I heard muffled sobs, sobs of a woman that I won't ever forget. She seemed dazed. I knew something was wrong. I hesitated, then walked back towards her.

"Is something wrong?" I asked.

She looked up at me with tear-filled eyes.

"Yes," she said.

"Is there anything I can do to help?" I offered.

"No," she replied, "but thank you."

I said something about hoping things would be okay and then continued on. I was further down the corridor but turned around thinking that I just couldn't leave her there. She was quite obviously in great distress.

"Would it help to talk?" I asked.

She forced a little smile and said yes. We then exchanged names. Her name was Peg and she told me her baby's name was Suzy. Peg and I went to my office, drank coffee and Peg used the phone to call home and figure out what she wanted to do. We talked for a long time. When she was getting up to leave, she turned to me.

"When I saw you coming back," she began, "I couldn't believe how kind a person you were. Thank you so much."

I smiled.

"Oh," she exclaimed, "Look at the time it is now and I've delayed you."

Peg had just shared her story with me. She spoke of her anxiety, her fear and of her love for her sick baby, Suzy. She had a lot of concerns about her other three young children at home. She talked of her husband, Brian, who was unemployed and coping badly with feelings of uselessness and inadequacy. He was finding it extremely frustrating to cope with the three children on his own at home. Peg spoke of her mother who was at this time dying in a nearby hospice. She remembered her brother, Karl, nineteen-years-old, who had committed suicide some four months previously. She spoke of her sister, Cathy, who was involved in a serious car accident that left her severely handicapped. There were other tragedies, I could go on and on.

Peg also spoke about her time spent at her baby's cotside. She told of how difficult she found it to sit and watch her precious baby struggle to hold on to life. Nevertheless, she spoke of her gratitude at being able to spend so much time at the Hospital, of being involved even in little ways in Suzy's treatment and being kept up-to-date with her progress. Peg talked about the sensitivity of the medical staff and of the graciousness and gentleness of the nursing staff.

I learned from her that, whenever she went for coffee or a meal, the canteen staff always addressed her personally and enquired about her baby's progress. Throughout the day, as Peg walked the corridors on route to the canteen or elsewhere, she was greeted with a smile or a hand wave by clerical staff, portering staff and administrative staff. This all meant a lot to her. A constant refrain on her lips that evening was, "Everyone is so kind."

But stop and think about it. If someone was standing in the funeral home summing up your life before your immortal remains, what would it mean to have him or her say you were indeed a kind person? Is anything more worthy than kindness?

As I took my leave of Peg that night and headed for home, there was no sound but the echo of my own footsteps. Later I smiled as I dozed off with a dawning insight that perhaps the only reason I was late coming off duty that particular night was to be kind to Peg.

Sr Therese Culhane, RSC is a former Chaplain at The Children's Hospital.

ANTICS AND ESCAPADES

DR JOHN F. MURPHY

The speciality of paediatrics, it must be said, was relatively slow to develop. Adult physicians viewed paediatricians with a certain note of suspicion, 'not quite one of us'. It was also regarded as a speciality with poor prospects and poor remuneration. Indeed it was commonly said even into the 1960s that anybody choosing paediatrics as a career needed to be slightly eccentric, be of independent means or to have married a rich wife!

From its inception Temple Street has had all the qualities that make a children's hospital unique. The informality and controlled chaos can be upsetting for those who have previously worked in an adult institution. However, the typical paediatric ward round in Top Flat, the main thoroughfare of the hospital, is particularly illuminating. While examination and diagnosis is important, frequently the first and biggest task is to find the child. He or she may be chasing up and down the corridor, hiding under someone else's bed or up in the playroom!

Children's playroom.

Tradition means that good or interesting characters have previously worked in the institution. And Temple Street certainly had its fair share of characters. One individual describes his consultant interview in the 1950s. It was very different to the current structure with a panel of experts, independent chairman and human resources supervision. His interview was in the back parlour with the Reverend Mother. He knew of her dislike of alcohol and he borrowed a pioneer pin from a distant relative. She was suitably impressed and he got the job. Much relieved, he ran out of the Hospital into Kavanagh's pub and ordered two pints. He realised that he had forgotten to remove the pioneer pin when he saw the barman stare and say, 'you must have been on the wagon a long time.'

Communication, empathy, sensitivity are not words that necessarily spring to mind when describing some of the older surgeons who attended the Hospital. One individual when doing his outpatients clinic sat on a high stool with his back to a large window. The patients had to look upwards into the bright glare when listening to him. The effect created a god-like aura and ensured that the consultation was short and that any silly or irritating questions were not asked. Informed consent and detailed explanations were also in short supply. One particularly 'cheeky' young mother dared to ask the attending surgeon what was exactly wrong with her child. She was told that 'the details were none of her business' and he would be writing in confidence to her GP in due course!

Eccentric behaviour was not confined to consultants and was on occasions encountered among the nursing sisters. One particular ward sister had a binding rule that everyone on the ward had to fall on their knees as soon as the bell struck for the Angelus. One young consultant, who had recently returned in a semi-pagan state after a period of training in England, did not fully appreciate the importance of this rule. When he failed to kneel at the appropriate moment, he was removed from the ward and not allowed back for two years.

There are professional mothers who have been attending the Hospital over many years with a succession of children. When their own grow up, they bring their grandchildren. These individuals know it all and have seen generations of doctors come and go. They are skilled at the quick remark. One consultant already late for his clinic came rushing through the waiting masses to the consulting room. Behind he heard a voice say, 'There goes Dr X late again, it'll be quick in and quick out today.'

The 'heartsink' mother is another feature. Although very nice, she has children with chronic, difficult problems for which doctors can do very little. A consultant had such a patient who turned up at the Hospital almost daily, although he had long since explored and exhausted all avenues of treatment. After yet another frustrating consultation, he mentioned to colleagues that he was shortly going into hospital for a knee operation and that he was looking forward to the rest. A few days later, lying on his bed in Cappagh Hospital, as he drifted out of the anaesthetic miasma, he saw a vaguely familiar figure standing at the end of the bed. The voice said, 'I brought little Mary up to the hospital to see you, but you weren't there. They told me you'd gone in for an operation so I said I'd come over to cheer you up.'

One time, a thirteen-year-old boy from the local flats developed a crush on an attractive junior doctor. He continually visited the Casualty with a variety of simulated complaints. When she tried to explain to him that he was healthy and need not attend anymore, he said that he really liked her and wanted to give her a present. She protested and said that she really didn't want anything. A few days later when she arrived into work, she found a 'nearly new' television set sitting on her desk with a little note, 'this is the best one I could get!'

Temple Street is a unique and treasured haven for sick children. Its beacon has shone brightly for a very long time. It has the affection, trust and support of the tens of thousands of children and their families who have received its services. I have every confidence that it will continue to serve and prosper both now and after its move to the Mater site.

Dr John F. Murphy is Consultant Paediatrician at The Children's Hospital and Consultant Neonatologist at The National Maternity Hospital, Holles Street, Dublin.

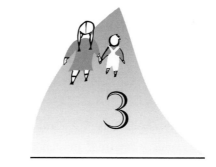

DEPARTMENTAL
DEVELOPMENTS

PATHOLOGY DEPARTMENT

DR PHILIP MAYNE

There was limited pathology services in The Children's Hospital prior to the appointment of Dr Seamus Cahalane in January 1961. His immediate predecessor, Dr Maureen Hayes, resigned as the pathologist to the Hospital following her marriage. Having qualified in medicine from University College Dublin and spending some time in Dublin, Dr Cahalane trained in paediatric pathology at the Henry Ford Hospital in Detroit. He later held the position of visiting WHO Fellow in Boston Children's Hospital before returning to Dublin, where he undertook a perinatal mortality survey in the Dublin maternity hospitals. This survey was funded by the Medical Research Council (MRC).

As a general pathologist Dr Cahalane was responsible for all aspects of the pathology service. In the early 1960s the Pathology Department was small, employing just four technicians (one in each of the four disciplines – histopathology, haematology, biochemistry and microbiology), a secretary and a cleaner.

NATIONAL NEWBORN SCREENING PROGRAMME

During the ensuing thirty years, Dr Cahalane was responsible for developing the National Newborn Screening Programme for inherited metabolic disorders and for establishing procedures for performing paediatric postmortem examinations on infants and children, who had died suddenly and unexpectedly.

Although Dr Cahalane had trained primarily as a histopathologist, he was particularly interested in developing micro-analytical methods for investigating small samples from children. It was this interest that brought him in contact with Dr Robert (Bob) Guthrie in 1961. Bob Guthrie had developed a simple microbiological method for measuring phenylalanine levels from a few drops of blood at his laboratory at the Children's Hospital at Buffalo, New York. At that time, blood phenylalanine levels were assayed in the Royal College of Surgeons in Ireland, the analysis requiring about 10 ml of blood irrespective of the size or age of the infant or child. In the late 1950s, Dr Doreen Murphy had been responsible for looking after a number of patients with phenylketonuria (PKU). Many of these children were severely mentally handicapped as the diagnosis was usually made late in the course of the disorder and dietary treatment was difficult to administer and monitor. A number of these children were diagnosed by the Diaper test, which involved dropping a solution of ferric chloride onto the infant's wet nappy and observing a colour change. This test only became positive at about six weeks of age, usually too late to prevent handicap. Approximately 70 per cent of infants born in the Dublin Health Authority area were screened by nurses using this test. In 1964, Dr Cahalane undertook a pilot study to determine the suitability of the Guthrie test to screen for PKU. Funded by the MRC, the study involved the screening of 10,000 infants born in the Coombe Hospital and the National Maternity Hospital. In total, one infant was detected as having PKU.

Teabreak in the lab c.1950 with fine bone china!

By 1964, three US states were using the Guthrie test for measuring blood phenylalanine levels, but only the state of Massachusetts was using the method to screen newborn infants. Following lengthy discussion and correspondence between Dr Cahalane and the Dublin Health Authority, in December 1964 the Department of Health agreed in principle to the proposal to introduce a screening programme for phenylketonuria using the Guthrie test. In early 1965, Dr Cahalane submitted a proposal to the National Health Council that such a programme, when implemented, should involve the entire newborn population. Although his proposal was agreed in principle, no decision was made as to the location of the screening programme. Various suggestions were put forward which included the tests being performed in the local hospital laboratory or centrally either in Cappagh Hospital or at the National Blood Transfusion Service. A note by the then Minister for Health, Mr Donogh O'Malley, TD, to the Secretary of the National Health Council, dated 29 June 1965, stated:

> *I agree that this service should be instituted, but I do not agree that it should be based on the National Blood Transfusion Service. I think it would be grossly unfair to Dr Cahalane. Could it not be conveyed to Health Authorities and to other voluntary hospitals that Temple Street is to be the centre for screening for phenylketonuria?*

It was subsequently agreed that the screening programme would be based at The Children's Hospital, Temple Street.

In 1965, it was estimated that the cost of screening every infant born in the Dublin catchment was approximately £4,500. This included a capital expenditure of £1,000 in addition to annual salaries of approximately £772 for a laboratory technician, £757 for a clerical officer and £525 for a clerk typist. Dr Cahalane agreed to undertake the programme within his terms of employment as the visiting pathologist to the Hospital. It was also estimated that it would cost between £650 and £750 to diagnose each case of PKU. At that time, the special diet for treating PKU patients was considered expensive, ranging from £4-7s-9d per week for a three-year-old child to £9-15s-5d per week for a nine-year-old child. In addition, it was noted that a child needed vitamins and bread made from special flour.

In late January 1966, the Chief Medical Officers, County Secretaries and County Managers were notified that the Minister of Health had completed arrangements with the Dublin Health Authority that The Children's Hospital, Temple Street would provide facilities for testing for the presence of phenylketonuria in newborn infants. The directive stated that the procedure would involve taking a few drops of blood by pinprick and transferring it to filter paper. The blood sample would normally be taken when the infant was five to nine-days-old. If a positive result was obtained from the screening test, further blood samples would be required for biochemical examination to establish accurately the blood phenylalanine level, and to verify that the child was affected by the disorder. When the presence of PKU was confirmed, the child would be placed under the care of a local paediatrician. The letter went on to state that 'the experience of the treatment of the defect is not yet sufficient to indicate how long it is necessary for children to remain on this diet.'

The total cost of the service, when related to the annual national birth rate of 60,000, was estimated to be approximately £6,000 – the previous estimate of £4,500 being based on the number of births in the Dublin catchment area. Finally, newborn screening for PKU began on 1 February 1966. Later that year, following discussion with the Superior General of the Irish Sisters of Charity, Prof Tom Kavanagh, visiting paediatrician to the Hospital, wrote to the Chief Medical Officer in the Department of Health requesting that the Department consider opening a special unit in Cappagh Hospital for the treatment of children with PKU. The principal reasoning for suggesting Cappagh Hospital was that it was felt at that time that children with PKU had an unusual susceptibility to infection. Therefore, it was considered undesirable to admit such cases to a general children's hospital. In January 1969, a meeting finally took place in the Customs House between representatives from The Children's Hospital (Mother Ann Eucharia, Dr Cahalane and Dr Doreen Murphy) and the Chief Medical Officer, Dr JC Joyce, and colleagues to discuss various aspects of the service. At that meeting it was agreed that there should be one national service for treating and monitoring PKU and that the current arrangements, whereby cases were being treated by individual paediatricians throughout the country, should discontinue. By 1971, it was estimated that approximately 90 per cent of infants were being screened.

Further approaches were made to the Dublin Health Authority to expand the service and it was agreed to increase the programme by the inclusion of a further four disorders. These conditions were introduced in 1971 and 1972. An additional technician was appointed at an annual salary of approximately £1400-0s-0d to cope with the increasing workload. It was noted at the time that 'it was planned to increase the scope to cover at least four other diseases of similar nature', although it is not recorded exactly which conditions these were.

In 1979, agreement was then reached with the Minister for Health, Mr Charles Haughey, TD, to initiate screening for congenital hypothyroidism, initially with the assistance of Dr Sylvia Dockeray and Dr Michael Cullen, consultant endocrinologist at St James's Hospital and Ms Catherine Mullins, senior biochemist within the Hospital. Thyroid scans were performed at St James's Hospital, but subsequently transferred to the X-ray Department within The Children's Hospital.

EXPANDING SERVICES

Ray O'Ceallaigh of the Microbiology Department undertook a pilot study in 1968 in collaboration with Mr Dan Kelly, consultant urologist, to determine the incidence of asymptomatic urinary tracts infection in children. This was funded by the MRC. In the early 1970s, this was expanded to screen schoolgirls attending North Dublin Inner City schools for urinary tract infections. The Variety Club of Ireland funded a mobile research laboratory and two nurses, who along with a technician visited the schools on a regular basis to collect samples and carry out tests. A Butlin Fellowship, in honour of Sir William Butlin, the Chief Barker of the Variety Club, was also established at the time to fund a paediatric trainee to undertake a three-year research study of paediatric nephrology.

The demands on the haematology service were also increasing following the introduction of standardised treatment protocols for leukaemia by Prof James Fennelly. These trials resulted in the improved life expectancy of children with leukaemia, and the number of children being nursed by Sister Margaret McMenamin and her nursing staff on St Michael's C Ward increased dramatically.

The introduction of peritoneal dialysis and a nephrology service following the appointment of Dr Denis Gill, and the continuing developments in the diagnosis and management of infants and children with inherited metabolic disorders significantly increased the workload on the Department of Clinical Biochemistry. The Variety Club also provided the funding for the purchase of a Locart amino acid analyser, while in the late 1980s the Hairdressers Association raised valuable funds for the Hospital to purchase a gas chromatogram/mass spectrometer for organic acid analysis. Unfortunately, this machine remained idle for a number of years because the laboratory did not have the funding to appoint staff with the scientific expertise to run the machine.

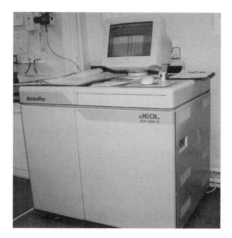

New equipment in the lab – Joel amino acid analyser (right) and GC/mass spectrometer (below).

STUDIES ON SUDDEN INFANT DEATHS

In the early 1970s, Dr Cahalane developed a particular interest in identifying the cause of death of infants and children who died suddenly and unexpectedly. As a result, he began performing detailed postmortem examinations. He was instrumental in introducing procedures for such examinations based on detailed consultation and collaboration with colleagues abroad. Also during the 1970s, Dr Cahalane organised a number of annual scientific symposia, inviting many distinguished clinicians and scientists. These symposia were subsequently organised by Prof Gill and continued up until the early 1990s.

NEW FACILITIES

By the late 1960s the Pathology Department was rapidly outgrowing its confined space on the ground floor adjacent to Casualty and beside St Michael's C Ward on the first floor. Discussions took place within the Hospital to fund and build new facilities to include an upgrading of the X-ray Department and pathology laboratories.

In August 1970, Sir William Butlin laid the foundation stone for the new X-ray Department on top of which the clinical research laboratories and the surgical operating theatres were subsequently built. Funds for the X-ray Department were raised by the Ladies Committee under the guidance of Mother Canisius, and subsequently by her successor, Mother Rectress – Sister Ann Eucharia. Once again, the Variety Club of Ireland contributed a significant portion of the funding and the Department of Health allocated £30,000 towards the cost of equipment. In May 1972, the X-ray Department moved into its new premises but no decision at that time was made to build the laboratory block or surgical theatres.

Initially, the Variety Club agreed to donate £30,000 towards the cost of the laboratories. However, during the following four years there was considerable uncertainty as to the future of the Hospital and the building costs estimates almost doubled between 1972 and 1974. Building of the new laboratories finally started in 1976, the Variety Club of Ireland having increased their contribution to in excess of £50,000. The Variety Club of Ireland Clinical Laboratories were officially opened in

February 1977 with a blessing by His Grace, the Archbishop of Dublin, Dr Dermot Ryan. Also, a dedicatory plaque was unveiled by the Chief Barker of the Variety Club of Ireland, Mr Rick Burke.

The new laboratory development included a number of specialist laboratories, and were described at the time as 'a fine new spacious laboratory replacing a tiny room, with modern equipment and up to six technicians [Haematology Laboratory], a clinical chemistry laboratory housing modern technology and equipment, expensive but essential, and staffed by graduate chemists and technicians – an upgrading of part of the old Microbiology laboratories to include Histopathology and the National Screening laboratory in addition to a Clinical Research laboratory and a conference room.'

In the ensuing years, the function of a number of these laboratories changed to allow for the further expansion of the pathology service. The conference room was incorporated into the Metabolic laboratory, while the Newborn Screening laboratory has been housed in a number of sites within the Hospital until its final move into space vacated by the Anthonian Press and Medical Records Department. These refurbished laboratories were opened by Dr Cahalane in February 1996 on the occasion of celebrating thirty years of newborn screening for phenylketonuria. Two years later, in 1998 the then Minister of Health, Mr Brian Cowen, TD, opened the National Meningococcal Reference Laboratories, the funding of which was secured by Dr Cafferkey from the Department of Health and Children.

In 1985 Mr John Joly, chief technologist to the laboratory and within the Histopathology Department, retired and was replaced by Mr Charles O'Neill. Having developed an interest in molecular biology, Charlie O'Neill took time out to complete a PhD at Trinity College Dublin and Baylor University, Texas. Indeed he has been instrumental in developing the molecular biology service in a number of the laboratories.

In 1989, Dr Ann Maloney was appointed consultant microbiologist, and three years later Dr Cahalane retired. He was succeeded by Dr Philip Mayne, consultant chemical pathologist who took over responsibility for the newborn screening laboratory and clinical chemistry, Dr Mary Cafferkey was appointed in 1993 following the resignation of Dr Maloney, and in 1994 Dr Deirdre Devaney was appointed consultant paediatric histopathologist. A consultant haematologist post was finally approved by Comhairle na nÓspidéal in 2000 and Dr Corrina McMahon was appointed in 2002. All four consultants hold joint appointments with the Rotunda Hospital and with other hospitals or medical schools.

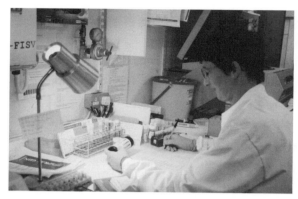

Anne O'Shea, biochemist.

COMPUTERISATION

The Pathology Department undertook an ambitious project to computerise the laboratories in 1995. A small working group lead by Anne O'Donoghue completed the complex project with the assistance of representatives from each department. This project has enabled the departments to cope with the ever-increasing number of requests and has facilitated the rapid retrieval of laboratory reports, both in the laboratories and on the wards, through a ward enquiry link.

From its relatively humble and small beginnings in the early 1960s, when just eight staff were employed, the Pathology Department has expanded over the past forty years to employ more than fifty members of staff. The Department has been lucky to have been able to employ enthusiastic, dedicated and loyal staff, all of whom have contributed to the successful development of the service. The Laboratory now provides a comprehensive paediatric pathology service, covering all four major disciplines, including molecular biology for the Hospital and local general practitioners, and through its national and tertiary referral services to the majority of hospitals throughout Ireland.

Dr Philip Mayne is Consultant Chemical Pathologist at The Children's Hospital.

ACCIDENT & EMERGENCY DEPARTMENT

Dr Peter Keenan

One could give a history of how the Emergency Department has evolved over the years, but the only appropriate thing one can say is that you never know what's going to happen next! Of course, what happens in the Emergency Department, of a dramatic nature, frequently delivers the unexpected to the wards, and in particular the Intensive Care Unit and Operating Theatre.

Sometimes, dramatic events evolve, happen, and resolve or are resolved solely in the Emergency Department. Such an event took place around 1994, one Friday afternoon at about 4.30 pm.

The Ambulance Service phoned in to say that three semi-conscious children were on their way – with no obvious causative background story available. We prepared our resuscitative equipment – tubes, masks, drips, etc. and prepared to receive them. Soon, wailing sirens and there they were – three toddlers – all under $4-3^1/_2$, 2, 1 – all three grey–blue in colour, vomiting and verging on unconsciousness. Accompanying them were their parents, both well themselves – this was important in terms of ruling out gas asphyxia in the household. (We rapidly established that the three kids had been put to bed by their parents shortly before becoming unwell.)

In parallel with immediate life-saving resuscitation (airway, breathing, circulation), a rapid history was taken from the two young parents, who stood anxiously by as up to fifteen doctors and nurses struggled to stay abreast of what was a rapidly deteriorating situation. Our patients were vomiting profusely and getting bluer by the minute; one stopped breathing and had to be incubated and manually bag and mask ventilated. It looked as though the other two were heading down the same road. And still there was no obvious clue – the three kids had been put to bed at approximately 5 pm by their parents – all three in the same room. Some ten to twenty minutes later, their mother heard a bottle hit the floor of the bedroom upstairs. (All three were commonly sent to bed with a bottle of warmed milk, sweetened with sugar.) Next, she heard vomiting and ran upstairs to find one of the three heaving and drowsy. Her two siblings didn't look too well to their mother – so she phoned 999, and here they were.

A frantic history was extracted, while resuscitation went on in this increasingly alarming scenario.

Had they been well prior to going to bed? *Yes.*

Had they any past history of illness? *The usual coughs and colds.*

Was either parent on drugs of any sort, in particular, Methadone? *No.*

Sure? *Not even a Panadol in the house.*

Absolutely sure? No antidepressants (deadly for children)? *Absolutely sure.*

Is there a stove, coal or gas in the house? *No.*

Were there any poisons? Where did both of the parents work? Could they have anything at home from work that might be relevant, which they might have overlooked? *I stay at home, my husband works in a butcher's.*

Anything from the butcher business – THINK? *No, except stuff for curing meat I use to keep ants away at home.*

What was it called? *Don't know – a white powder.*

Off went Dad and the police, sirens screaming, to the house on the North Circular Road to get the stuff. Soon after, in came the phone call – the meat curing powder was identified, and when the mother heard where it had been found, she realised she had put it in the kid's bottles instead of sugar. By now, two of the three children were unconscious, and one of which was receiving cardiac massage. All three were blue as Bangor slates.

Someone had suggested methhemoglobinemia (exceedingly rare) as a treatment possibility. This is a condition which all doctors learn about (then forget!) where haemoglobin (the oxygen carrying molecule in red blood cells) becomes altered chemically, rendering it unable to carry oxygen, giving the victims blueness of blood (seen visibly as blue lips) and increasing unconsciousness as the brain is starved of oxygen.

Many doctors, even at the intensive care end of medicine, retire after many years of busy practice, without encountering this dramatic, rare condition. There is a known antidote, which is rapidly effective in this condition – methylene blue. A hurried search turned up some vials in our ICU. The antidote was rapidly obtained and injected intravenously into our unfortunate three – two of whom by now were intubated and bag ventilated. The third was semi-conscious but breathing spontaneously.

Over the next twenty minutes, in front of the amazed (and deeply relieved) eyes of anaesthetists, nurses, emergency doctors, all three began to shed the deep blueness of their lips and nail beds and one by one regained consciousness. Such a dramatic turnabout from a seemingly fatal free-fall is not common in previously healthy people of any age, and even rarer in acute paediatrics. All three stayed in overnight and went home the next day, perfectly well.

Opening of the new Accident & Emergency Department on 17 July 2001, left to right, Mr Paul Cunniffe, Dr Peter Keenan, Mr Micheál Martin, Minister for Health and Children, Dr John Murphy, Bishop Jim Moriarty and Mr Justice Richard Johnson.

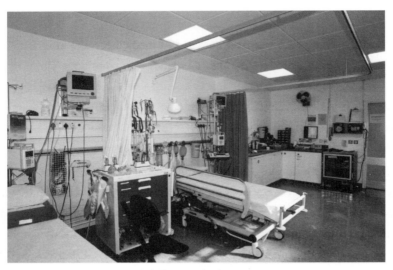

A & E resuscitation unit.

Analyses of situations such as this invite many 'what ifs' from the hindsight comfort of a good result. What if Mother hadn't heard the bottle hit the floor or the children began to vomit? What if there had been loud TV or radio? What if Dad had brought the offending chemical home and forgot to tell Mother? What if he wasn't there when the kids fell ill? What if…what if...and so on.

Emergency situations are determined in their evolution by accidental coincidence (sometimes preventable, sometimes not). Sometimes the outcome is also affected for good or bad by coincidence.

Dr Peter Keenan is Consultant in Accident & Emergency at The Children's Hospital.

NEUROLOGY DEPARTMENT

DR MARY KING

Caring for children with acute and chronic neurological disorders has always been central to the care provided at The Children's Hospital. Prior to the appointment of a paediatric neurologist, such children were looked after by general paediatricians, some of whom had a particular interest in neurological disorders. Among the most prominent of these was the late Prof Neil O'Doherty. Prof Niall V. O'Donohue, consultant paediatric neurologist at Our Lady's Hospital for Sick Children, Crumlin and professor of paediatrics at Trinity College Dublin provided an acute consultation and some outpatient service for these children. The late Mr Fergus Donovan, consultant neurosurgeon, developed the specialty paediatric neurosurgery at this Hospital. However, it was not until the late 1980s that the comprehensive Paediatric Neurology Service for children began, with the appointment of a consultant paediatric neurologist, Dr Mary King. This included the development of a Clinical Neurophysiology Service providing EEG (for children with suspect epilepsy, coma, etc.), evoked potentials (looking at visual pathways) and EMG, and nerve conduction studies (for children with muscle disease).

The Department of Clinical and Neurophysiology opened in 1987 under the direction of Dr Mary King with a staff of one consultant, one neurophysiology technician, one secretary and one shared junior doctor. The first EEG machine was purchased with funds raised by the pupils in nearby Belvedere College. Over the last fifteen years, the Department has expanded to its present complement of sixteen members of staff. In 1995, Dr Bryan Lynch took up the post of paediatric neurologist with particular interest in epilepsy surgery. This involved the evaluation of patients with severe epilepsy who may be suitable candidates for surgical intervention. Such children may require invasive (inside the skull, on the surface of the brain) EEG recordings over several days in hospital. As this may be very stressful for the families and children, a stand-alone video EEG inpatient unit was developed at the Hospital.

The appointment of the first clinical nurse specialist in paediatric neurology in 1994, Therese Nestor, had a major impact on the direction of development of the neurology services. This was at a time when the video EEG and monitoring room was being considered and coincided with a rapid expansion in the number of staff within the Department. Over the years, Therese and her clinical nurse specialist colleagues, Suzanne Keily, Daisy O'Donnell and Saundra Nolan have provided a consultation service to inpatients and outpatients, have run nurse-led clinics for adolescents with epilepsy, and produced information leaflets for patients with epilepsy, particularly adolescents. A unique development has been the designation of one of the clinical nurse specialists to provide liaison for families of children with severe neurological disorders who have major nursing needs and whose parents wish to care for them at home. Through liaison with the families and the support groups, particularly the Jack and Gill Foundation, Nurse for Daniel, etc., Saundra has helped many of our families care for their children at home. The nurses have close links with the various support groups including Brainwave, Muscular Dystrophy Ireland, Neurofibromatosis Association, etc.

Video EEG unit with Odette O'Flaherty.

Children with neurological disorders usually require multidisciplinary evaluation and over the last decade, we have been very fortunate to have the input of specialised paediatric neuropsychology, speech and language therapy, social worker, occupational therapy and physiotherapy. In addition, some patients may require very specialised dietician input for management of epilepsy, and to this end, Catriona Hensey, senior dietician, was appointed. Furthermore, the Clinical Neurophysiology Department has expanded to include one chief, one senior and a student technician.

Children with neurological disorders require not only the input from a paediatric neurologist but also from a team specialised in disability, both learning and physical. The Neurology Department has excellent links with the Physical Disability Services at the Central Remedial Clinic in Clontarf, directed by Dr Owen Hensey. Similar links are with the Learning Disability Service at St Michael's House and St Vincent's Centre, Navan Road. This ensures a co-ordinated treatment follow-up programme for children with disability.

The Department works closely with the specialised psychiatry team at St Frances' Clinic. Specialised clinics are carried out for epilepsy surgery evaluation, and a movement disorder clinic is held with Dr Tim Lynch, consultant adult neurologist at the Mater Hospital. On reaching adulthood, patients are transferred to Beaumont Hospital or the Mater Hospital, depending on their needs.

In the last few years, the most important development for outpatients has been the arrival of the magnetic resonance imaging (MRI) on site. The implications of this facility for early diagnosis and treatment are obvious, but it has the additional benefit for families of not having to travel out of the hospital.

The administrative support of Antoinette Cloak and Amanda Bracken has been immeasurable over these years as has the support of the Executive Council of the Hospital.

The Neurology Department has a strong research tradition with regular publications in the field of neonatal neurology, neurometabolic and other disorders. The Department looks forward to continuing improvement in the service provided to children with neurological disease and eagerly awaits the relocation to the new Mater site.

Dr Mary King is Consultant Paediatric Neurologist at The Children's Hospital.

KIDNEY UNIT

PROF DENIS GILL

The Hospital's interest in developing the specialty of paediatric nephrology was initiated in the 1970s. During that period, Dr Seamus Cahalane and Mr Dan Kelly obtained funding from Billy Butlin for a research fellow in paediatric nephrology. Denis Gill obtained this post and spent several years training at Guy's Hospital, London and the Children's Hospital, Philadelphia. In 1978, he was appointed to The Children's Hospital and soon after got an appointment to Jervis Street Hospital, which was then the national dialysis and transplant centre. In the early 1980s, a peritoneal dialysis programme was set up with Sister Margaret McMenamin, who was then in charge of St Michael's C Ward. This was the first peritoneal dialysis programme for children in this country. At the same time, children were being prepared and presented for transplantation at Jervis Street.

Initially, the dialysis programme provided a form of peritoneal dialysis called continuous ambulatory peritoneal dialysis (CAPD). Children had a dialysis catheter inserted in their abdomen and were dialysed four times a day at home by their parents. This enabled us to dialyse infants, and indeed a small number of children were dialysed from the neonatal period to transplantation. However, by the end of 1980s, a move forward to automated peritoneal dialysis using overnight machines was made. This is now the normal form of dialysis offered to children. They go about their normal daily activities and have peritoneal dialysis while asleep at home at night on an automated cycling machine. Certainly, this was a great psychosocial improvement. The purpose of the dialysis was to bridge the gap between kidney failure and transplantation.

A good collaborative service between The Children's Hospital and Jervis Street, later Beaumont Hospital, was established. Initially, Mr Sean Hanson did most of the children's transplants with the assistance of Mr Denis Murphy. In more recent years,

Mr David Hickey with his colleagues performed the kidney transplants. Children were prepared for transplant at Temple Street and are cared for at both hospitals following transplant.

Over the years the kidney team has gradually grown and now includes a specialised sister, a dialysis nurse, a nephrology nurse, plus the services of a dietitian, psychologist, schoolteachers, play specialists and social worker. This multidisciplinary team has met weekly for many years to exchange information, ideas and support facilities for the children and their families. We were very lucky in the early 1990s to get involved with the Barrettstown Hole in the Wall Gang project. This has enabled us to provide wonderful holidays and breaks for the children for ten days in the summer period. It has proved a most beneficial intervention for the children particularly, but for their families as well. We have been very grateful for the assistance given by Baxter Healthcare.

The team over the years has produced a booklet – *Kidney Kids* – which informs young children about kidney failure, kidney transplantation and its consequences. This was published by the Irish Kidney Association and is still in print. In the 1980s, the team also produced the video *Bertie Bean and the Kidney Machine*, with the purpose of informing children about peritoneal dialysis. This video was shown at international meetings and was well received in its time.

St Michael's Unit has been blessed by a series of interested, involved and innovative ward sisters, namely Margaret McMenamin, Cliona Cronin, Cathy Hennerby, Fiona McHugh and currently Linda Ennis. In 2000, a second nephrologist, Dr Atif Awan was appointed. Perhaps the most important development has been the appointment of the renal nurse specialist, the post being initiated by Claire Ryan. The post has greatly improved communication and continuity of care for these children and their families. In 1999, a dialysis nurse, Marie O'Connell, was appointed, enabling us to provide a weekday dialysis service and this is now providing treatment for two children. The Unit has also moved into haemofiltration and plans to establish plasma exchange in the near future. We have also over the years been kept busy with acute renal failure by our metabolic colleagues.

The twenty years or so of our Kidney Unit have been gratifying and quite a large number of our children have graduated into adulthood with functioning grafts, good health and hopefully gratitude. Indeed, we recently had one of our earlier patients bringing back their own children to be seen by us.

We have been greatly helped by parents whose support, particularly in fundraising, has been remarkable. Money has been received from many groups of parents for the purchase of machines, support or education, and sending staff members to conferences. In particular, we would like to mention the Martin family, the McKeever family, the Conlon family, the O'Brien family, the Bourke family and many others who have demonstrated their support through a variety of fundraising initiatives enabling us to buy machines, monitors and other equipment.

In August 2001, two children who had been attending the hospital from birth received successful transplants, aged four years and nine years, respectively. This is what the service is all about. Thus far, over one hundred children from The Children's Hospital, Temple Street have been prepared for and received transplants at Beaumont Hospital.

Prof Denis Gill is Professor of Paediatric Medicine at The Children's Hospital.

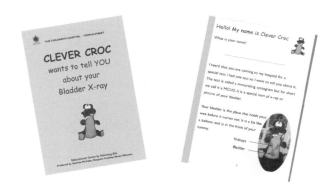

Specially designed leaflets and brochures like Clever Croc help to explain to children what is involved in, for example, a bladder X-ray.

ST ULTAN'S METABOLIC UNIT

DR EILEEN NAUGHTEN

A dults and children from all over Ireland who inherit metabolic disorders are looked after by the Metabolic Unit. The Metabolic Unit as it currently exists was formally acknowledged by the Department of Health in 1986 with the appointment of Dr Eileen Naughten. Previously, the Unit had evolved under the direction of Dr Doreen Murphy who died in 2001 in her nineties. Dr Murphy was a general paediatrician who developed an interest in the treatment of phenylketonuria when it became available in the late 1950s.

TREATMENT FOR METABOLIC DISORDERS

Phenylketonuria was a cause of severe mental handicap and had a very high incidence among the Irish population. In common with other general paediatricians around Ireland, Dr Murphy identified some children with delayed development who were subsequently shown to have phenylketonuria. When treatment became available in the early 1950s, the foodstuffs were extremely expensive and very difficult to ingest. Faced with a possible cure for phenylketonuria, Dr Murphy and some of her colleagues in Dublin tried to implement the diet in various families with varying degrees of success. Gradually over the years, her colleagues referred a number of patients to the care of Dr Murphy and she accumulated the largest collection of patients with phenylketonuria in the country.

The patients attended Dr Murphy in a portacabin in Temple Street, where she initially had a dietitian, Miss Gilmore, who was the hospital dietitian at the time. Following Miss Gilmore's retirement in 1970, the hospital acknowledged the work being done by Dr Murphy and appointed Ms Margery Kellett whose responsibility was to look after the

[123]

diet of individuals with phenylketonuria. During the 1970s, individuals with homocystinuria were identified and also commenced on diet. Ms Kellett also looked after these patients with Dr Murphy.

Around this time patients with galactosaemia were also being identified and colleagues referred these to Dr Murphy from all over Ireland. In those days, there was no official base in the Hospital for the Metabolic Unit and Ms Kellett was situated in the Records Office where she did her own typing and looked after the charts for all patients who required treatment. Clinics were held each Tuesday and Thursday. The personality of Dr Murphy was stamped all over these clinic days. Patients were seen on a walk-in basis in a portacabin situated where St Frances' Clinic currently exists (now the car park) and the clinic commenced at 10 am and finished at 1 pm. By 1977 when Ms Kellett had been replaced by Ms Ita Saul, the clinic had moved to a portacabin adjacent to stores at the back of the Hospital and near the old nursing home and car park. Ms Saul was the first full-time appointment in October 1977. When Ms Kellett commenced her appointment forty patients were attending. And by the time she left in 1977, there were 140 attending.

Dr Murphy retired in 1984 and staff at that time consisted of Ms Saul and Dr Eileen Naughten who was appointed in a locum capacity and given a permanent appointment in 1986. Dr Naughten was a UCG graduate, who having completed her internship in Galway, trained in Oxford and London. She was granted a Sir William Butlin Fellowship by Temple Street Hospital, became a Harvard fellow and studied in Boston and then returned to London before taking up her appointment in 1984. When she was appointed in 1984, there were 240 patients with phenylketonuria, six with maple syrup urine disease, twelve with homocystinuria and miscellaneous other conditions.

ST BRIGID'S WARD

In the late 1980s a new group of disorders was identified, which explained some cot deaths, causes of cerebral palsy and handicap. This resulted in a sharp increase in patients and referrals and a new era in prevention of these conditions. By the time St Ultan's Metabolic Unit opened in 1994, further requests for staffing had already been submitted. A ward for metabolic disorders – St Brigid's Ward – was opened in June

1993 staffed by nurses who were dedicated to working with individuals with acute inherited metabolic disorders. By now the emphasis had moved away from phenylketonuria, where the condition was dealt principally as an outpatient condition. Conditions requiring hospital admission were maple syrup urine, organic acidemias, including fat oxidation defects, urea cycle defects and children with hypoglycaemia, near miss cot death episodes, etc.

STAFFING

The Unit gradually expanded, and a second consultant was appointed in May 1993. Dr Geoffrey Thompson came from Melbourne but returned to Australia within the year. Dr Paul Thornton, a UCD graduate, subsequently took his place in January 1996. Dr Thornton combined paediatric endocrinology with inherited metabolic disorders. He worked in the Unit for approximately three years before returning to the University of Philadelphia, Pennsylvania. He is now director of the Diabetic Unit in Philadelphia Sick Children's Hospital. By 2002 there were three consultants, Dr Eileen Naughten, Dr Eileen Treacy and Dr Sufin Yap. Dr Eileen Treacy was director of the Biochemical Genetics Unit, McGill University, Montreal for five years before taking up her appointment in Ireland. A TCD graduate, she extensively researched the role variation of a drug and toxin metabolising gene. Dr Sufin Yap was appointed in 2001 and has an MD in homocystinuria based on the outcome in patients who were treated for twenty-five years by Dr Doreen Murphy. This outcome is considered the gold standard internationally and many units try to emulate it.

Various doctors played a major role in helping the Unit over the years. Dr Ahmad Monavari worked for nine years in the Unit as a registrar and then as a locum consultant. Dr Patrick Ward worked as a research fellow, Dr Berry Kiely spent a year as a research fellow, while Dr Gillian Darling also spent several years as a research fellow. Publications from the Unit number over one hundred in peer review journals.

The staff in the Unit have increased, initially from one dietitian with one physician to a total of twenty-two staff members comprising specialised nursing staff, five full-time dietitians, two psychologists, two social workers, two registrars for the outpatient clinic and one registrar for inpatient care, one play therapist, one house officer and five administrative staff. The patient numbers registered in the Unit that need life care has now reached 1539 and many new conditions have been identified because of advances in technology. The laboratory staff have increased and they now have two full-time amino acid analysers working seven days per week.

Since September 1993, organic acidaemia high-risk screening is being carried out in the laboratory. The rate of identification within the Irish community of inherited disorders shows that we have an increased incidence of most of these disorders, mainly aminoacidopathies and organic acidaemias. A secretary was appointed to take over the dietetic typing, in addition to the medical typing in 1986.

NATIONWIDE METABOLIC SCREENING

A major milestone in Irish public health was the introduction of screening, which commenced nationwide in 1966. Initially, Dr Murphy had met with Dr Bob Guthrie at a meeting in Lisbon and returned to Dublin carrying his screening kit. She persuaded Dr Seamus Cahalane to carry out some tests, which he subsequently did. He tested the methodology, found it to be reliable and then carried out a pilot study in Dublin. The rate of identification of positive cases with phenylketonuria was so great that he approached the then Minister for Health, Mr Donogh O'Malley, TD, about establishing nationwide screening. This was carried out on a 'shoe string' budget and was the pride of the Irish health services. There is no doubt that the implementation of screening was one of the most advantageous and fruitful public health measures in Irish medicine. The rate of identification of individuals with phenylketonuria was approximately twenty-five cases per year. Identifying babies who had no adverse effects from the biochemical elevation of phenylalanine created an opportunity for early treatment, and they were started on diet. It was hoped that they would achieve full normal intellect. This was subsequently shown to be the case.

Over the years screening for other conditions was added into the screening programme, namely homocystinuria in 1971, galactosaemia in 1972, maple syrup urine disease in 1972. Hypothyroidism was later added to the screening in 1979.

The patient numbers were such that it was obvious that further dietetic support was needed. Applications were made to the Department of Health in 1984, which were finally granted in 1991. The rate of identification of individuals with inherited metabolic disorders by this time had escalated and further applications were already with the Departments of Health and Finance for an increase in staffing.

Dr Murphy was a most enlightened physician who achieved major success for her patients with these inherited disorders. She set the highest standards of care. She recommended the diet should not stop, contrary to common opinion at the time, and published this in the late 1960s. She also noted that the diets and their cost were prohibitive for families. The cost of a diet for one individual with phenylketonuria was £600 at a time when the salary of a principal in a National School was £900. Some of the families who attended had six and seven family members with phenylketonuria. At that time, Dr Murphy approached the Department of Health and succeeded in getting the Medical Card implemented for individuals who require treatment for phenylketonuria, and subsequently for other inherited disorders. This was a major achievement for her patients. The combination of the excellent treatment and screening programme set the Irish services apart in the area of preventative medicine and public health. This model was copied in other centres, as we were the first country to have national screening.

IRISH SOCIETY FOR INHERITED METABOLIC DISORDERS

During the late 1980s the Irish Society for Inherited Metabolic Disorders (ISIMD) was formed with Dr Naughten as president. Mr John Flynn was chairman, his wife Imelda sat on the Committee representing MSUD. Mr Declan O'Bric was secretary and his late wife, Mary, was on the Committee. They, along with Mr Brendan Molloy and his wife Lillian, represented PKU. Mrs Margaret McMenamin represented galactosaemia. Mrs Ann Kennedy, who was treasurer, represented homocystinuria along with Mr and Mrs Kennedy of Cork.

They organised fundraising, held regular meetings, contributed to the newsletter which commenced in 1985. Educational days were held in Dublin and Cork which usually consisted of a lecture on advances in PKU, etc. followed by tea and special dietary foods. Ms Saul organised Christmas parties and cookery demonstrations each year, whereas Ms Kellett organised Easter egg distribution, a tradition that continues to this day. These events were always well attended and supported by parents.

ST ULTAN'S INFANT HOSPITAL

A further position was held by Dr Murphy with St Ultan's Infant Hospital located on Charlemont Street, Dublin 2. When this hospital was closed in the 1980s, it was decided that the money from its sale would be divided among the children's services in Dublin. Priority was given to services for mothers and their children and Dr Naughten submitted an essay which won for the current Metabolic Unit, the sum of £183,000. The Department of Health capped the £183,000 and on 18 May 1994, the Metabolic Unit, which exists in Temple Street today, was opened by the then Minister for Health and Children, Mr Brendan Howlin, TD. Retaining the name of St Ultan was part of the legal agreement with the surviving members of the Board of St Ultan's Infant Hospital.

At the official opening of St Ultan's Metabolic Unit in May 1994, Judge Richard Johnson, chairman of the Board of Management, with Dr Eileen Naughten and Mr Brendan Howlin, Minister for Health and Children.

Some individuals with handicap were being looked after at the time in St Anthony's Hospital, which was also under the aegis of the Sisters of Charity. In addition, individuals were being referred from institutions for the handicapped throughout Ireland and these were being given a trial of diet. This trial of diet consisted of a minimum of two years and proved extremely successful with a lessening of nurse–patient ratio and an improvement in the quality of life to individuals who would never be able to lead an independent existence. This work still continues under the care of Ms Margery Kellett and Dr Naughten.

The Metabolic Unit in Temple Street has an international reputation based on excellent patient care and good outcome. It is highly respected among its peers in the discipline and we have many visitors from other centres. There are many publications from the Unit each year and the staff are invited to present the work of the Unit at meetings in the United States, the United Kingdom and Europe. The recognition and appointment of metabolic specialists nurses in 1999 has been a major advance. Certainly, this will be increased in the near future as home visits and home teaching is the way that metabolic disorders will go in the future.

Nurse Celine Stenson has worked with patients with these disorders since 1992 and has provided a continuity of care and knowledge which has been of great benefit to all the patients. The recognition and appointment of metabolic specialist nurses in 1999 has been a major advance. The way forward for the future lies in peripheral clinics, home visits and home teaching which have been established over the past three to four years.

Dr Eileen Naughten is Consultant in Metabolic Medicine at The Children's Hospital.

ST CLARE'S UNIT

KIERAN MCGRATH
DEIRDRE HAYES

S t Clare Unit is one of two specialist child sexual abuse units based in Dublin paediatric hospitals – the other being St Louise's Unit in Our Lady's Hospital for Sick Children, Crumlin. St Clare's Unit serves the catchment area north of the River Liffey, comprising the northside of Dublin, City and County. It opened in 1988 and in that time over 5,000 children referrals for assessment of concerns in relation to child sexual abuse have been made to the service. In 1999 a therapy service for children who have been sexually abused was also established. This was funded by the Department of Health and Children and provided for extra staff and a new building.

From the outset, St Clare's has sought to provide a broad, family-based service with the focus not just on whether abuse may or may not have occurred, but also on the overall psychosocial needs of the child and his/her family. To this end, a multidisciplinary team employing social workers and clinical psychologists – with a child psychiatrist as unit head – was seen as the appropriate model. Later a psychotherapist and art therapist were added to the complement of staff.

Over the period that St Clare's Unit has been operational, child sexual abuse, and the abuse of children in general, has become a highly charged social and political issue. The Unit has always tried to contribute to the development of practice and knowledge in this area, nationally as well as at local level. For example, in co-operation with our colleagues in St Louise's we have organised an annual conference each year since 1989. We have also been involved in providing training courses to other professionals, including Health Board staff and the Gardaí. In addition, we have made significant contributions in the establishment of the Support Network for Professionals in Child Protection (since 1991), which has been a pioneer in the development of services for adolescents who sexually offend. St Clare's staff have also sat as members of government-appointed committees on issues, such as Child Prostitution and the Video Evidence Committee.

Entrance to St Clare's Unit.

Through attendance at international conferences, St Clare's Unit has managed to develop links with international organisations and professionals, particularly the best of researchers and practitioners from North America and the UK, who can contribute to the enhancement of Irish practice. Furthermore, a major contribution was made to organising the International Congress of the International Association for the Prevention of Child Abuse and Neglect (ISPCAN) in 1996.

In all our endeavours we have aspired to create in St Clare's Unit a centre of excellence where children, who may have been sexually abused, receive the best care that can be provided.

Kieran McGrath is acting Clinical Director of St Clare's Unit and Deirdre Hayes is acting Principal Social Worker at The Children's Hospital.

PHYSIOTHERAPY DEPARTMENT

DEIRDRE SHEEHAN

What the Physiotherapy Department in our hospital lacks in terms of space, it more than makes up for in personality, one of the main reasons to attract me to a short-term locum post here almost six years ago. During this time, I have seen huge developments in both staffing levels and the service provided by a very dedicated group of people. Although, I just wish that so many of us weren't called Deirdre.

The Physiotherapy Department was well and truly established in 1967 with the arrival of Ms Evelyn Doyle from St Mary's Hospital in Baldoyle. Having previously worked with polio sufferers, she brought her expertise in rehabilitation with her. In The Children's Hospital, however, she did a little bit of everything, working single-handedly six days a week for many years. She is still remembered by many of the Hospital staff and some of our patients and their families.

The current staff began to arrive in the late 1980s, in the form of Mary Little, and in dribs and drabs throughout the 1990s. Most who came stayed to propel the Department into the 21st century, led by Deirdre Molloy, our acting physiotherapy manager.

Although covertly known as the 'physioterrorists', we would like to think that we coax, cajole, motivate and perhaps inspire our young charges to achieve goals that will ultimately make their lives more full and enjoyable. Whilst very aware that initially we remind children of their injury or illness, we would like to think that ultimately we help them to forget or come to terms with it.

For some children and their families, however, childhood and adolescence is punctuated by repeated visits to hospital. These families are the ones that we all get to know very well. While providing physical care for the child who is unwell, we also form part of the support system for the whole family. The support systems of this Hospital are unique, fostered by the Hospital ethos and enhanced by its small size. Much as we may carp about the difficulties associated with working in a very confined environment, we recognise that this is one of the reasons why the bush telegraph works so efficiently. It enables us to keep up to date with the lives and progress of the children with whom we are involved.

A refurbished and updated Physiotherapy Department in 2002.

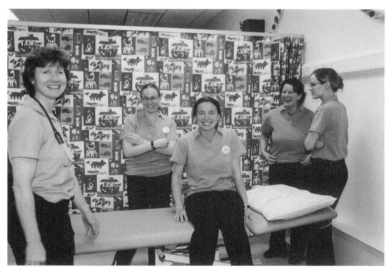

Physiotherapy staff, left to right, Deirdre Sheehan, Joanne Gracie,
Eileen Maguire, Deirdre Fahy and Ruth Skinner.

Our little home in the Outpatients Department is currently undergoing a major extension. A space that was originally used by only one member of staff has been bursting at the seams over the past few years, with seven physiotherapists making demands on the space and equipment during the past year. While we ourselves did a lot of knocking on doors, we are very grateful for all the support we have received from our colleagues. Our new Department will remain our home until the Hospital moves to its new site on the Mater Hospital Campus. I do hope that in the course of the relocation, all the features that make the Hospital such an enjoyable setting in which to work will travel with us.

Ms Deirdre Sheehan is Physiotherapist at The Children's Hospital.

OCCUPATIONAL HEALTH DEPARTMENT

ELEANOR HONAHAN

Occupational health is primarily concerned with the effects of work on health and health on work. The specialty of occupational health is comparatively new to The Children's Hospital. Prior to 1998, a hepatitis B vaccination clinic was run by a staff nurse in the Outpatients Department, one morning a week for hospital employees. In February 1998 the speciality received full recognition when Ms Paula Rafter was employed full-time as the occupational health advisor (OHA) and the Occupational Health Department was thus set up.

At the outset, an occupational health booklet was introduced giving details of the aims, objectives and services being offered by the Department. First and foremost, the vaccination clinic facility was increased to three times a week at varying times to accommodate both day and night staff. Manual handling training for non-nursing employees commenced in April 1998. A workshop introducing risk assessment to managers was run in May/June 1998 with the issue of a dedicated form for assistance in the carrying out of such assessments.

Dr Blanaid Hayes, occupational health physician, commenced employment in May 1998 for one three-hour session per week. Prior to this, Dr Mary Cafferkey, consultant microbiologist, assisted in occupational health issues. Initially, the OHA shared a room with the infection control sister, though for the purpose of running the vaccination clinics, the OHA continued to use the treatment room in the Outpatient Department. In July 1998, the Department moved to where it is now currently situated – one small room adjacent to the convent and on the second floor of the School of Nursing. Over time, the services provided by the Department developed to include sickness/absence referrals, accidents/incidents follow-up and risk assessments. The vaccination clinics continued but were now inclusive of screening for immunity to the infectious diseases of childhood, in addition to the administration of the Mantoux to detect whether or not BCG was required for staff protection against exposure to tuberculosis.

Subsequent developments in the Department were made in terms of staff and equipment. In December 1999, Ms Eleanor Honahan joined the Department. Dr Mary McMahon took over from Dr Blanaid Hayes in July 2000, continuing at one three-hour session per week and in the same month, Ms Phil Mulligan, became part-time secretary in the Department. In November 2000, due to demands on the service, Dr Mahon's hours increased to two three-hour sessions per week. Ms Claire Hand joined the Department in November 2001 bringing the OHA complement to one-and-a-half.

In recent years, specialised equipment was purchased which greatly enhanced the services provided by the Department. The Accutrend GC Meter was purchased in September 2000 for use in inhouse health promotion events. January 2001 saw the arrival of the Keystone VS-II for vision screening, thus enabling compliance with current legislation in regard to display screen equipment. An automated sphygmomanometer was purchased in 2001 also for use in health promotion events.

Since 1998 the range of services has undoubtedly expanded and become more diverse. The human resource staff pre-employments began in 1999, with the exception of doctors. This service was further developed to include all pre-employments for nursing administration. Since January 2001, vision screening has been carried out at pre-employments.

Health Promotion and Education Days also figure highly in the Department's calendar, ranging from advice on smoking cessation to sun awareness. An Employee Assistance Programme is in place whereby employees may refer themselves to the Occupational Health Department for advice and support. If it is thought that he/she may benefit from professional outside counselling, a referral is offered through the Department. Overall, the Department has responded to the needs of staff and requirements of legislation and hopes to continue to provide such services well into the future.

Ms Eleanor Honahan is Occupational Health Advisor at The Children's Hospital.

THE PRIMARY SCHOOL

MARY CHAMBERS
MARY McCARRON

There has been a Primary School in Temple Street since 1968, evolving through the years from a one-teacher unit to its present status of three permanent teachers – Mary Chambers, Ciara Somers and Mary McCarron – one special needs assistant and one classroom assistant.

The Primary School is funded by the Department of Education and Science and since the establishment of Boards of Management in Primary Schools in 1976, has been managed by our own Board of Management representing the patron – the Archbishop of Dublin – parents and teaching staff. This Board is re-elected every three years and subject to the 1998 Education Act. We would like to record our thanks to all who contributed on the various boards throughout the years.

The school is an integral part of the Hospital and operates a child-centred, multidisciplinary approach to education. As a hospital school we come under the rubric of Special Education. Our current enrolment is thirty-five pupils, which are facilitated in one classroom and one resource room. However, children confined to bed are taught individually in their wards.

Mary McCarron describes a day in the life of one of our hospital teachers:

It's 9.30 am on a busy ward at the top of the house in a children's hospital. Breakfast is eaten. Drugs round is over. Doctors have been and gone. All the mobile non-infectious patients of school-going age, i.e. from four years up are being shepherded down two flights of stairs to the classroom by our classroom assistant and special needs assistant. Meanwhile downstairs, nurses arrive at the classroom from other wards with children suffering from ailments such as renal failure, diabetes, cystic fibrosis, epilepsy, metabolic disorders, asthma, etc. The classroom teacher is ready to begin a day's work.

Together in the classroom are the junior infants starting school, children from all the classes in the Primary School and post-primary pupils. The latter includes those preparing for State exams, and some who have dropped out of the mainstream education system altogether and whose only link with education nowadays is a brief visit to the Hospital School when in for treatment. There are children from many different cultural backgrounds; immigrants, refugees, Travellers, etc. Then to add more variety, we have the special pupils, those who are physically challenged and arrive in wheelchairs or on crutches, those who are visually challenged and many with multiple disabilities. All are welcome.

Pupils on the ward consist of children who must have complete bedrest and children who are too sick or sore to go to the classroom. Some of them are on drips, others are on traction following orthopaedic operations, and then others again who because of their illness cannot mix with other sick children, but are otherwise well enough for school.

I greet the staff nurse who runs the ward. We discuss the children who are ready for school and any who have special needs. Here you are very much part of a team. Unlike a normal school where you have sole charge of your pupils, there is a holistic approach to the treatment of the children in hospital, and education is one part of this approach. You are known by your first name and everywhere in the hospital you will hear children calling you, looking for books, schoolwork, etc., and saying goodbye as they tear out of the wards on their way home.

Hospital School helps bridge a gap. Long-term patients and recurrent admissions are our priority pupils. These are the children who can very easily fall behind in their education and slip through the system because of interruptions in their schooling. Many find it hard to settle back into school after a prolonged stay in hospital. Our school records include details of their education, so that when they arrive appropriate work can be assigned to them, and there is a minimum of delay in setting the wheels in motion. With parents' permission, I often have to contact the Home School for relevant information so that we can provide a quality service. These children know the teachers and look out for our familiar faces. They are the patients who know to pack their schoolbooks as well as their pyjamas.

At the bedside, I have to give priority to medical personnel. One has to be very flexible. Work is constantly interrupted by physiotherapists, dieticians, nurse specialists, teams of doctors, medical students doing exams, children called for X-ray...the list is endless. Sometimes it means taking a step back and waiting, often it means visiting the next child and returning later, and in some cases I end up leaving a little work at the bedside.

Parents are delighted to see you arrive. Here they play a very active role in their child's education. It gives them an insight into how their child is learning and sometimes it can show gaps, which they were unaware of previously. It gives them a chance to take a break. The time is long when one has to sit by a sick child all day and sometimes all night as well.

Because many of these children have had interrupted schooling, there are many stories of failure to achieve their potential at school and much of the work tends to be remedial in both English and Maths. Teaching goes on at many different levels. There is the social interaction with the special children, some cannot speak or move but recognise my voice from reading them stories and meeting me daily on the ward.

A highlight of the school year is the day when the Primary School presents the annual Christmas play. This is staged in the Hospital chapel and is a popular event with members of staff. Don't laugh when I say that last year Joseph only arrived at the eleventh hour. Mary had rehearsed with amazing diligence. Her costume fitted her beautifully. Alas, on the day, poor Mary was rigged up to drips and confined to bed and so another Mary had to be found instantly.

Being a partner in the treatment of sick children is very rewarding and my job is made all the easier by the excellent co-operation I receive from the Hospital staff.

Ms Mary Chambers is Principal, while Ms Mary McCarron is a Teacher at The Primary School, in The Children's Hospital.

ST FRANCES' CLINIC SCHOOL

MARY COUNIHAN

St Frances' Clinic School provides a window of opportunity to discover and develop each child's unfolding potential, recognising the Religious Sisters of Charity tradition, it works in collaboration with parents and partners involved in the education process.

With this motto, the special primary school opened its doors on 14 January 1967 with nine children enrolled. The first school principal was Mary Grant and some years later in February 1971, Aideen Jeffers took over as principal. Then in March 1974, Mary Counihan took up the post and is the current principal.

From the outset, the school was set up as a diagnostic class for children with severe speech and language difficulties and associated behaviour and learning difficulties. Funded by the Department of Education and Science, the school is managed by our Board of Management, which includes a parent representative, a teacher, a community representative and a patron's representative.

The school has evolved and changed considerably since its foundation. The current pupil–teacher ratio is six children to one teacher. A full-time assistant/play specialist is also employed to work in the school. Marion Anderson has held this post for twenty years. The school is supported by a dedicated multidisciplinary team. Moreover, the approach is child-centred with the emphasis on developing each child's specific needs.

Close links are developed with parents, and parenting programmes are tailored to meet their needs. We offer a varied curriculum which includes much of the new national school primary infant curriculum. Other new developments include a music project initiated in the spring of 2002. For this project, we joined with the pupils of the Mater Special School and the Outreach Education Team from the National Concert Hall.

In 2001 we were fortunate to have an occupational therapist, Clare O'Donoghue working with us. This year, we have plans for an Art Project with the Education Team from the Municipal Art Gallery.

Over the last few years, we have developed close links with the Hospital School and playroom. For example, the children join together in the annual Christmas play and numerous other activities during the school year. A special thanks goes to all the staff in the Hospital and Clinic who have been so supportive to us over the years.

Ms Mary Counihan is Principal at St Frances' Clinic Special School.

Waiting area of St Frances' Clinic.

THE CHAPLAINCY SERVICE

SR ANNE CURRY, RSC
SR ANN FORREST, RSC

The Chaplaincy Department within the hospital represents a very specific and professional discipline. It works with other professional disciplines in providing an overall or holistic service that is geared towards patient care and ministry to the family. Chaplaincy is about expressing respect and care, about listening in a compassionate way and about helping to create a space, which recognises the spiritual needs of the patient and the family. Religious ministry activities promote the development of individual charisms and facilitate healing, reconciliation and the celebration of life's journey. People are offered a form of care, which reflects a vision of faith. However, in responding to the religious needs of the patients of different denominations, the chaplains uphold the patient's right to choose to participate, and respect for religious freedom and personal convictions are maintained.

Spiritual care of the child and family has always been part of the service in this Hospital. Initially, the Hospital was included in the parish of the Pro-Cathedral and the priests from the parish were chaplains to the Hospital. They came when called to administer the sacraments of baptism, confirmation and reconciliation, to conduct funeral services and celebrate the eucharist. With the formation of St Francis Xavier's Church, Gardiner Street as a parish, the parish clergy now provide sacramental ministry. The records of the administration of the sacraments over the years are preserved in volumes and are a tribute to the Sisters who scripted them. We have used them on many an occasion to provide information for people requesting details of their baptism and confirmation.

Over the years, the delivery of healthcare underwent change and development and a more holistic approach to caring was adopted. The Sisters of Charity were aware of the signs of the times and a number of Sisters studied Theology and Clinical Pastoral Education and became certified as chaplains with the Healthcare Chaplaincy Board of Ireland. At present, two Sisters serve as chaplains in the Hospital.

The chaplains function as members of a multidisciplinary team and receive referrals from other relevant staff/departments/services in relation to patient care. The chaplains carry out religious ministry activities to encompass worship, prayer and other liturgical celebrations that are in keeping with the concept of inclusion. Pastoral visitation of the clinical areas, accompaniment and pastoral caring throughout the patient's stay in hospital are part of the daily routine. Listening, praying with the family where appropriate, blessing prayers and the administration of the sacrament of baptism when requested, form part of this ministry. The service provided is patient-led and visitation continues in accordance with the wishes of the family. Pastoral caring is continued during long-term illness/disability/terminal illness/death and dying. In the case of death, continuity in pastoral caring is given throughout the reposing period in the mortuary. Guidance and support in funeral arrangements in conjunction with other relevant staff is offered, where necessary, and a funeral service brings this part of caring to a dignified conclusion.

Chaplains are available to staff members and provide a supportive presence to staff in the front line, especially those involved in the acute areas of the Hospital. They are also involved in the education of staff in-service and induction courses on an ongoing basis.

This account may give the reader some idea of what is involved in the service provided by the chaplains in the world of healthcare today. One thing is clear, the profile of the chaplain has changed over the years. It is therefore necessary that they be spiritually, emotionally and intellectually equipped to bring the compassionate healing power of Christ into a broken world of the 21st century.

PAX VOBIS

Sr Anne Curry, RSC and Sr Ann Forrest, RSC are both Chaplains to the Children's Hospital.

BOARD OF MANAGEMENT

FIONN MACCUMHAILL

I was sitting in the Castle Hotel one sunny morning in 1996, opening my mail. Among the usual mountain of post there was an envelope marked Religious Sisters of Charity. As I was looking at the envelope, I instinctively reached for my chequebook, thinking, 'they're at it again!' But I was wrong. It was a letter inviting me to join the Board of Management of The Children's Hospital, Temple Street. I was honoured.

Memories came flooding back to me. I was reared in the suburb of Whitehall and Temple Street was part of our young lives. As a child it seemed to me that people went to a hospital and never came back. But Temple Street was different. My boyhood friends went there with mysterious illnesses, painful appendices, or to have their tonsils removed but everyone came back miraculously cured and better for the experience. We all reverently claimed that Mother Mary Aikenhead was the patron saint of aspirin. Undoubtedly, there was a certain magic in the neighbourhood – friendly Dubliners playing outside their new flats, traders getting ready to go to Moore Street. It was a lively place that delivered miracles on demand.

Having accepted the invitation, I went to visit Sr Bernadette who showed me around the Hospital and spoke about the 1986 plan to build a new hospital. I was determined that we would have a good hospital with fully functional buildings that were brightly lit and painted, with no degradation of service or rundown facilities until the day we entered a new hospital. Today the 'Rexine' bench is no longer there, replaced by a modern reception with electric doors. We have a new Accident & Emergency Unit with Day Ward and a bright, cheerful courtyard garden, courtesy of the Ark Cultural Trust, who involved local children in its design.

During my first few months as a board member, it became clear that all was not well with the immediate neighbourhood. The crime rate was rising, the streets littered with broken glass, pavements broken and the once-vibrant cheery community now looked very grim. A chance remark by Mary Finlay gave me an idea. A public meeting was held, attended by the then Minister for State at the Department of Justice, Mr Austin Currie. At the meeting the chairman, Judge Richard Johnson, said rather eloquently, 'The people in this room can solve the problem.'

From that meeting a committee was formed which I chaired, comprising public representatives, local residents, the Department of Health and Children, the City Architects Department, the newly formed North City Business Association, An Garda Síochána, and a member of the Board of Management. It met regularly with a view to improving the environment and security of the local area of the Hospital. This united effort proved successful and as Dr Veronica Donoghue remarked, 'The whole thing is the difference between night and day.'

To this day I still marvel at the unselfish service of my fellow board members, nuns and colleagues. Also, when I think of the great supporters that the Hospital has had over the years, my thoughts turn to An Taoiseach, Bertie Ahern. Apart from his commitment to the new children's hospital, his personal generosity is boundless. Having donated his much-prized Sylvester Stallone jacket to a fundraising auction, it raised over €50,000. You could say he gave the jacket off his back for the Hospital! Certainly for me, the sun always seems to shine in this part of the city centre.

Fionn MacCumhaill is a member of the Board of Management of The Children Hospital since 1996.

*Ark Cultural Trust garden
at Temple Street.*

4

STORIES OF
CHILDREN

ON MY ROUNDS

PAT MAHON

My first impression of the Hospital was one of amazement, because it looked nothing like a hospital but an old Georgian house. I first stayed at the Hospital at the age of fourteen and had my first visit to theatre. I was not very impressed by the outfit that I had to wear – a blue gown, white see-through cap and white see-through underpants. I wore the pants once, and never again – the nurses could see too much!

I had many stays in the ICU and made numerous friends in the nursing staff. My first stay was for a week during which I couldn't speak, and so I wrote everything down on a notepad – jokes, worries, demands and emotions. I still have them and some of the contents are quite funny, but unsuitable for reproduction here! I remember once writing a note to an anesthetist, who was on call, asking why she had street clothes on and did she wash her hands before touching me, since everyone else had to wear white aprons and washed with hibiscrub.

As I got older, I used to keep the night staff company as well as the day staff. I would go on my 'rounds' from ward to ward staying up until about 3 am in the morning. My mother used to say that I came home for a rest and always suffered 'withdrawal' after Temple Street Hospital. I often accompanied the night sister as she visited each ward. And I always visited ICU after report for the chats and cups of tea.

One day I was feeling very depressed, as I was due to go to theatre. Just before the time I was allocated, I 'disappeared'. Because I really didn't want to be found, I kept on the move. First, I went to the Day Ward, which was just above Phil's, and from there out to the garden. Eventually, Nurse Lucy Nugent, who knew me so well, found me in ICU. She talked me into going to theatre at about half past five that evening.

School in the Hospital was situated above Phil's, but being 14+ I was not very enthusiastic about it. Many attempts were made by the poor teacher to get me there, but I knew my surroundings so well that I was able to skip off and not be found. I even told the teacher one day that I'd left school altogether.

Having to go to theatre so often, I got to know the porters very well and Neil in particular was a buddy. He taught me how to do wheelies in the wheelchairs, which was a major achievement for me at that time. While I was in Phil's it was Mary, and then Gillian in Surgical Flat, who looked after my food, and 'more' or 'different' was never a problem. I often visited the kitchens and they would get salads from downstairs for me, always smiling and never saying no.

Throughout my stays in Temple Street, I became very good friends with the doctors and called them by their first names. One day in Surgical Flat, Mr Russell came and I called him John. Sister was there and horrified to hear me speak to him in that way. She thought it was very disrespectful and told me to address him as 'Mr Russell'. Of course, I replied 'Yes, Sister.'

Liam Claffey was 'my' anesthetist and was very good to me. Each time I went to theatre, as I would 'fall off', I would ask him to 'look after me' and he always did. He always had time for a chat and would often appear if I was 'down' to have those few words of encouragement. I will always be grateful to him for that, which meant a lot at the time. I would have loved to have had a go on his bike! I heard all about the bike from my parents who met him one night after one of my operations and they thought he was a courier – they were trying to cheer me up!

I am very thankful to the entire staff of Temple Street Hospital for contributing to my return to health, because as I see it, everyone had a hand in that one way or another. I think of you all very often. Because much of my early teenage years was spent at the Hospital, you also influenced my outlook on many things. I have many memories, some wonderful and some not so wonderful, which I'll have for the rest of my life. Thank you all very much.

EYESIGHT – A FAMILY AFFAIR

JOE & GRÁINNE GERAGHTY

Monday, 12 June 1990 is a date many Irish people remember. While Ireland made their first ever appearance at the World Cup in Italy we had other thoughts – we made our first ever appearance at Temple Street! It was a very traumatic day. Claire, our first baby, was admitted to Michael's B for eye surgery in the form of cataract removal. Both of us were also born with cataracts, and I [Joe] am a carrier myself.

For Claire, it was to be the first of many eye operations but, for us, it was the most difficult. As new and anxious parents we explained Claire's eating and sleeping habits and even went into her thirteen-day medical history. Colic! However, we soon discovered Claire was a healthy, well-cared-for child, in a ward with some extremely sick infants, many in incubators.

Little did we know on that never-to-be-forgotten Monday that we were to meet two people who would play a major role in the future of our family. The first of these was Sister Bernie Lanigan, eye clinic administrator *par excellence*. The other was Mr Michael O'Keefe, gentleman and genius eye surgeon. When Claire had her first operation, both went out of their way to explain all that was going on. Both were equally helpful when the other eye was operated on one week later.

Two years later, baby number two – Christopher – arrived. He too found himself in Michael's B within a fortnight of birth for the same two operations. Then in November of that year, complications set in and Christopher spent much of that month and December in Temple Street. Glaucoma developed in his left eye. Again, the O'Keefe/Lanigan partnership sorted him – and us – out!

As Christopher returned for a post-operation check-up there was to be a strange quirk of fate. Mr O'Keefe noticed that I [Gráinne] also had glaucoma. While Michael O'Keefe helped me fight it off for a few years, eventually, I lost all my eyesight.

We continued to go in and out of Temple Street throughout the 1990s. First, it was Claire in January 1996 for glaucoma, and later the new baby, Eleanor, in September 1996 for cataracts also. Indeed, Eleanor was back and forth every two months thereafter. By April 1998, we had a fourth baby, Katie, and she couldn't be left out of the Temple Street initiation – cataracts again!

At one point in 1998 we had Eleanor and Katie both in hospital at the same time. These days, on the Day Ward, thanks to the help of Sister Lanigan, we regularly have two children with same-day appointments lying in beds side by side.

The year 1999 saw Christopher back in the month of August with glaucoma. In 2001, Claire returned for perhaps her biggest operation. Evidence was emerging that she was losing her eyesight and urgent action was necessary. Mr O'Keefe fought it off successfully with procedures, including trebeculectomy, laser treatment and the insertion of an artificial valve to release the build-up of fluid in her right eye.

For more than eleven years our family have grown up with Temple Street. We have got to know, and get on with, many of the staff. Two memories remain. At a young age, Claire absolutely hated and bawled out Mrs Madden, the now retired Day Ward sister, each time she put in those stinging eye drops. But now we can say they are great friends.

Our final memory goes back to the very first week in June 1990. The chaplain dropped in to Michael's B and asked us how we were doing. Terrible, we told him. Well, he says, the parents always suffer more than the children. These were words of great solace. Finally, our thanks goes to the Hospital administration and staff at Temple Street, whose work we greatly appreciate.

AN APERT'S VIEW

SIMON & CAROL GAVIN

Not many of you will be familiar with the term Apert's syndrome, and until a little over five years ago, neither were we! It was following the birth of our third child Cian – a boy – who came along to join his two sisters, Aoife and Shauna. At the time of Cian's arrival, we were living in Dubai. And while the Middle East, particularly Dubai, is well advanced medically, they were unprepared (as indeed were we) for a case of Apert's syndrome.

So, you may ask, what is this syndrome? Well, in layman's terms, and with apologies to Michael Early (much more about him later) for any medical inaccuracies, Apert's syndrome is a 'fluke' of a genetic disorder that affects all bone growth and development throughout the body. The most obvious effects are in the shape of the head (a lot of Apert's have premature fusion of the fontanelles, and are prone to raised intercranial pressure, many requiring a shunt), recessed midface, with protuberant eyes, and syndactly of the fingers and toes. Syndactly is like webbing, but with the distinction that, particularly in the fingers, the bones, blood supplies, and nerve endings are all fused along with the skin. These kids have a lot of directly related problems – feeding difficulties as babies, hearing difficulties, problems with pressure on the optic nerve, snoring/sleep apnoea, to name but a few.

We have been incredibly lucky with Cian in terms of his medical needs. Many with his condition require much more medical support and surgical intervention than he has needed. They need a highly specialist and multidisciplinary team to monitor and intervene, such as that provided in a Craniofacial Unit. There are, I believe, only three or four of these units in the UK, and until fairly recently, none in Ireland. Michael Earley, and the other specialists in Temple Street, changed all that. Mr Alcutt, Mr

Small, Mr O'Keefe, Mr McManus, Prof Gill, and various other specialists (please forgive any omissions, poor memory being the cause), made Temple Street the Mecca of craniofacial disorder treatment in Ireland.

I cannot thank Michael enough for, apart from being an amazing surgeon, he has never exhibited anything other than the utmost courtesy in dealing with Cian as a patient, and Carol and myself as parents. However, I think the attitude of all the consultants may be best summed up by a story about Mr McManus. We were worried about Cian not walking by eighteen months, and had a number of consultations with Mr McManus. He not only reassured us in terms of Cian's development orthopaedically (and he was right – now five, Cian can hold his own in a race with his siblings), but also on one occasion declared, '…that child does not need an appointment to see me. I'm here every Monday morning – just tell the nurse I said it's okay.' That humanity applied, without exception, across the board.

As you may guess though, we did spend a fair amount of time in Temple Street Outpatients, particularly in the beginning. Staff there were thinking about hanging a 'Reserved' sign over our favourite corner. It did take some time to realise that, although the day specified on the appointment card was going to be accurate, the time thereon would not bear any relationship to GMT. God bless *The Irish Times* crossword (or any crossword for that matter) and curses on the Naas Road traffic.

Again, though I railed against the appointment system (but have now developed my own defence mechanism), I have nothing but admiration for the Outpatient Department staff, who, always under pressure, are unfailingly never less than good humoured, even when faced with irate, stroppy and agitated parents – but we won't mention any names! Again, a story illustrates. To see one consultant a visit is normal. Occasionally, you can be lucky and fit in two. Three is to be dreamed of. However, one afternoon, there was four *in situ* (or five, my memory is failing) consultants/registrars that Cian needed to touch base with for check-ups. Talk about shuttle diplomacy – we were no sooner out of one consultation than we were into the next. We were even slotted in somewhere else while we waited the forty-five minutes for eye drops to take effect.

Although, we have been lucky with Cian in terms of the amount of surgery he has required, we have had some experience of overnights in Temple Street. The first – a whisker away from a life support machine with respiratory problems on our first Christmas back home in Ireland. Later another stay for the same – but with a less serious problem. Also a few days of surgeries for middle ear cleanouts and grommets, and what I consider the 'Majors'. Cian now has a little finger on each hand where none existed previously – take a bow, James Small. He is also the proud possessor of three titanium mesh plates in his head which hold together the remodelling job carried out by Michael Earley. It may be just another day at the office for the surgeon, but as a layman, the skill and courage of these people never ceases to amaze me.

We have been all over the place – Top Flat, Surgical Flat, Intensive Care, High Dependency Unit – you name it, we've been there. And when they say that nursing is a vocation, they are obviously referring to the staff of Temple Street as the prime example. Working in overcrowded and cramped conditions imposed by the strictures of an old building, they look after not only the 'run of the mill' (if there is such a thing) cases, but also cases that would cause a stone to weep, and in a way that makes every child special. Again, my nature being what it is, there have been times when the frustrations of a situation have built up, but the nurses have proven that they are as adept at soothing ruffled adult feathers as they are at 'lullabying' a distressed child to sleep.

My mother had a saying for when the going got a bit tough, 'You think you're badly off with no shoes until you see the man with no feet.' That's my personal lesson from Temple Street. I have met kids and parents who have borne burdens that no person should be asked to take on, but who have met the challenge head on with amazing courage and good humour. Their fortitude is matched by the professionalism, dedication, understanding, and kindness of the staff. Temple Street Hospital is no more than a collection of buildings. The people are truly what make the difference.

BEST SUPPORTING ACTRESS

GWENDOLINE BAKER

Our association with Temple Street Hospital effectively began on 29 May 1992, the day our first child Kyrsten was born. She looked a normal, healthy 8 lb 1 oz baby but was found to have Pierre Robin Syndrome. This manifested itself in a cleft of the soft palate with the only outward sign being a small recessed chin. The cleft prevented her creating the vacuum required to suck. Enter Eilis Murphy. She arrived at the Intensive Care Unit in the Rotunda Hospital armed with various bottles and suggestions about how teats could be modified. For the next few months every feed took two hours. Kyrsten was fed, partly by nasogastric tube and partly drip-fed using a bottle, in the hope that this would encourage her to use at least some of the muscles important for later speech development. At six months she had her palate repaired by Mr O'Riain and we had our miracle baby who could drink from a bottle!

Triona Sweeney, specialist speech therapist, closely monitored Kyrsten's development from the outset, and advised us on how best to help her at home. This, combined with regular speech therapy sessions with our local speech therapist, Celia Nichol, has been invaluable in helping to minimise nasal turbulence and improve clarity. However, a videofluoroscopy showed the need for a pharingoplasty operation, which Mr Earley performed in 1998. Again, this was a turning point, as over the next few months there was a marked improvement in her speech. Indeed, it is a tribute to the efforts of all involved in her care that she recently won the Best Supporting Actress award for her performance in a play at a local feis!

Hearing problems often go hand in hand with this condition, and from birth Kyrsten has had numerous ear infections, with the fluid present causing varying degrees of hearing loss. Ms Cuffe continues to test her hearing regularly. Also Mr Blayney has inserted grommets on four separate occasions when her ability to hear was particularly diminished, and at a time when poor hearing was likely to adversely affect speech development. As time goes on, she still needs to be reviewed frequently.

On 10 October 1996, our second daughter, Zoë, was born with the same condition. By then the squeezable Meade Johnson bottle was available, so our feeding difficulties were greatly alleviated. Otherwise, she followed very much in the footsteps of her sister. Mr Earley repaired her palate in 1997. Mr Blayney inserted grommets on three occasions. She continues to receive speech therapy and is currently being assessed as to whether or not a pharingoplasty will be required.

Both girls' experiences of their numerous visits to Temple Street have been incredibly positive. Mostly their visits are to clinics where the toys and books in the waiting room are a great distraction, and occasionally they might be treated to an ice-cream from the canteen downstairs! Stays in hospital have meant receiving Mum's undivided attention for hours on end, playing all those games we haven't often time to play at home, with visits to the playroom as they begin to recover.

Every member of staff we've met has made a great effort to put children at ease and to explain to them (and to their parents) exactly what will happen or what is required of them. The Hospital's child-centred approach means that a parent can accompany a child to theatre and remain with them until the anaesthetic has taken effect. We've had ten visits there to date! Of particular importance is the team approach taken by all the specialists involved in the care of a cleft-palate child. We will never cease to be grateful for all the care and attention our children have already received and will undoubtedly continue to receive in the future.

ALEXEI, THE BOY FROM MINSK

HELEN BARRETT

It was 8 January 1996 and the first day back at school following the Christmas holidays. The usual post-Christmas blues, however, were replaced this time by butterflies in the stomach and a preoccupation that had nothing to do with the start of a new term. The reason? My husband Chris and I had volunteered to care for a very sick six-month-old baby boy from Minsk, Belarus. And he was due to arrive that very day!

We had first heard about him a few weeks earlier when my sister Adi Roche returned from one of her many visits to the homes of abandoned babies in the radiation-affected areas of post-Chernobyl, Belarus. When Adi had been introduced to this little boy, Alexei, she was initially horrified at what she saw. There was a huge tumour growing out from his left eye socket plus several other related problems, including strange finger-like growths from his chin. The director of the institution, where Alexei had been placed immediately after birth, understood the seriousness of his condition, which was life-threatening, and thus pleaded for him to be brought to Ireland. As soon as Adi and Ali Hewson – patron of Adi's charity, Chernobyl Children's Project – returned to Shannon, they contacted Temple Street where Michael Earley unhesitatingly agreed to assess Alexei as soon as he could be brought to Ireland. So the process of Alexei's life changing was immediately begun and Adi travelled to Minsk to accompany him on his journey. It was a daunting experience as the poor little mite was ill on the plane and Adi terrified that the tumour would bleed, or worse still, burst!

The initial plan was for Alexei to come and get to know us. Needless to say, at this point we had only seen a photograph of him. As we waited anxiously on that fateful day, Adi phoned en route from Shannon to say that a bed had become available in Temple Street and that he was being brought there immediately. We made our way to the

Hospital in an acute state of nerves. I think I had only ever been in the Casualty Department once or twice when I had occasion to bring some child who'd had an accident in the schoolyard. I'll never forget the moment when Adi brought Alexei to meet us in his borrowed carrycot. We were completely overwhelmed by this little 'angel', so quiet and so helpless, and in spite of the horrific tumour, so alert and gorgeous. We were smitten. It was love at first sight!

That night Alexei was seen by Michael Earley, that wonderful man who had the courage to agree to gather a team of experts together to perform the major surgery so urgently needed. His positive attitude to Alexei's development was also very reassuring. So began our relationship with Temple Street Children's Hospital and the Craniofacial Unit.

When Alexei was finally admitted some weeks later, we were actually quite relieved as the tumour was beginning to cause him a lot of distress, and it was becoming increasingly difficult for Chris to dress it. We were heartbroken to part with him on the one hand, but also so happy with the love and care provided by the wonderful staff at the Hospital. Alexei won everybody's heart, and when I subsequently met Michael Earley's wife at a charity fashion show I wasn't surprised to hear that the Earley family felt sure that Michael would arrive home with Alexei under his arm one day!

It was immediately after the surgery that we were told about the Craniofacial Clinic, and indeed warned not to be too upset when we would attend for the first time. At this point, it was still housed in prefabs and always overcrowded and stuffy. My impressions however weren't about the building, but more about the huge number of children and parents, who like us had so many reasons to be grateful for the genius of Mr Earley and Dr Alcutt. We also found the Clinic a friendly place to be with everybody chatting to each other, which made the waiting time fly by.

After about two visits to the prefabs, the lovely new clinic was opened and that was a huge change, with lots to stimulate the children. By now, Alexei had progressed so well that we were down to just yearly visits. We look forward to these very much, as it's lovely to meet again with the marvellous nurses who knew Alexei as a tiny, sick, sad, little baby. It's a great feeling when they comment on how much he's grown and how well he's doing. And, of course, Alexei himself sees Temple Street as 'his' hospital and Mr Earley as 'his' doctor! Indeed, whenever he becomes anxious about people commenting on the fact that he has only one eye and wonders about getting another one, I invariably answer with a 'Let's talk to Mr Earley about that when we see him again.' He's always satisfied with that!

While Alexei is not in need of immediate surgery, we know that there will probably be further reconstruction work to be done when he gets older. Thankfully, because our experiences have all been positive ones, I don't think Alexei will have any worries. He certainly skips into the Craniofacial Clinic quite happily every time. As he begins to understand the sequence of events that have brought him to this place, he will have every reason to be grateful for it, because without it I wouldn't now be writing this story.

A GREAT NATIONAL INSTITUTION

ANTHONY & MARGARET O'CONNOR

A dowdy building somewhere at the top of O'Connell Street, Dublin where youngsters had their tonsils removed and various medical ailments attended to.

In 1979 this was my perception of Temple Street Hospital. My only direct experience with the institution occurred when, on busy shopping trips in Dublin, I was accosted by assertive strangers rattling a box under my nose, with pleadings for a donation for the Temple Street Hospital – which always seemed to be in dire need of funds. How wrong I was. Over Christmas 1979, my perception was abruptly changed. Our third child, Michael, was born with the condition known as cleft lip and palate. As parents, we were devastated by the news.

For those unfamiliar with the condition, it occurs during the early stages of pregnancy where the roof of the infant's mouth fails to fuse properly resulting in a large cavity, or cleft. In addition, the upper lip may be malformed, and the infant's nasal, speech and hearing functions impaired. After birth, feeding the infant is particularly difficult and requires professional help and ongoing medical assessment and evaluation.

In March 1980, Temple Street Hospital came to our rescue and became an integral part of our lives for many years. The first procedure, three months after birth, was to repair the upper lip and nose. It was left to Mr Seamus O'Riain and his team to perform the operation. I shall never forget the night before surgery when we said goodnight to Michael in his crib and left him in the safe custody of the Hospital staff. We prayed all night for a successful outcome to the operation and, thankfully, it was.

After surgery, we visited our infant son and marvelled at the work of the plastic surgery team who had transformed Michael's face. At long last the gaping upper lip was replaced with new tissue and, save for a small scar on the upper lip, his facial features looked inexplicably normal and brilliant. He even managed a smile, which brought tears to our eyes.

For the next eight years or so, Temple Street became a central part of our lives with constant visits to day clinics for medical assessment and many, many hours spent in St Frances' Clinic for speech therapy, where Triona Sweeney led the team. Normal speech is difficult, to say the least, because surgery realigns facial muscles and tissue needed for the formation and creation of speech. Hence the services of a professional speech therapist are mandatory. As parents, we spent many hours at home implementing the various prescribed speech exercises. Failure to abide by these exercises could have resulted in a serious inability to communicate by the spoken word – so we had no choice in the matter. Each weekday afternoon, without deviation, school exercises were combined with speech therapy exercises as part of a normal curriculum.

Of late, I began to realise why years earlier, collectors in the streets of Dublin sought funds to improve the lot of Temple Street and rattled collection boxes under my nose. The recently exposed tax avoidance scandals of the 1970s and 1980s ensured that institutions, like Temple Street Hospital, were deprived of Government funding and resources at that critical time. It is impossible to quantify, but realistic to state that many infirm children with many and varied ailments suffered intolerably as a result of this sleaze.

In 1980, the Cleft Lip and Palate Association was formed and I became secretary. A voluntary body of parents and friends, we campaigned for improved medical resources and treatment for cleft children, and organised seminars and public lectures to disseminate knowledge on the condition. We consulted, and campaigned successfully, with the Department of Health and Children and various government agencies. Over the past twenty years or so, the Association has worked closely with Temple Street, and raised funds for much needed equipment for the Hospital to improve specific services.

As I look back on the early eighties, I can only marvel at Temple Street Hospital, which has attained the status of a great national institution. The quality of care and medical services provided are on a par with the best in the world. The dedication of the nuns who administrated the hospital, and the quality of surgery and service, nursing and aftercare, the professionalism of the multidisciplined teams and the positive and enriching qualities and attitude of all concerned, defies description and is a credit to all concerned.

As parents, we shall always be in the debt of Temple Street Hospital. Words cannot express our gratitude other than to convey our deep appreciation to all concerned – those retired and those still practising – with particular mention of Mr Seamus O'Riain, Mr Michael Earley and Dr Triona Sweeney and all the staff in the Cleft Palate Unit.

We have only to look at our son, who is now aged twenty-two years, to wonder at the miracles that Temple Street Hospital performed for him over many years, and the quality of life, and speech, which he now enjoys. We can only wish all in Temple Street Hospital every success for the future.

IN A FUN WAY

Niamh Ní Dhoibhilín

My name is Niamh and I'm twelve years of age and have a condition called neurofibromatosis. I am a patient in Temple Street Hospital and have been since I was ten months old. I was two and a half years old when I was first diagnosed with neurofibromatosis. This condition causes tumours to grow anywhere on nerve endings around the body.

I have had seventeen operations and most of them were in Temple Street Hospital. Others were in Beaumont and the National Orthopaedic Hospital, Stanmore, London. If I were to choose my favourite of the three, it would definitely be Temple Street for the staff there are incredibly nice, comforting, helpful and – most of all – fun! Some of my main doctors are Mr David Alcutt, Dr Mary King, Dr Liam Claffey, Mr Michael Early, Mr Michael O'Keefe and Mr Frank MacManus. Rachel and Olive are my social workers. Valerie McGrath is my nurse from ENT and Deirdre Sheehan is my physiotherapist.

I've stayed in Philomena's, Michael's B, Top Flat, ICU, HDU, Surgical Flat, the Day Ward – just about the lot – even Casualty for a while. There are so many good nurses who take care of me – too many to mention! Everyone is so nice and caring. The doctors ask me for my opinion as well as Mum and Dad. Dr Claffey always takes loads of pictures of me with his good camera when I am in hospital. Valerie and Lucy look after my trachy and my dressing. Deirdre, my physio, is not just a physio but a fantastic friend too. If I ever need physio, Deirdre does it in a fun way, so that it does not seem like physio at all. I am now getting nurses out to the house. If I want to go to school, they bring me there or sometimes they bring me shopping (both in my wheelchair).

Sometimes we even stay at home and do different activities. Their names are Laura, Linda, Sandra and the new nurse who is coming soon is called Catherine.

I also get a teacher from the school, who brings out the laptop with her. So when I am finished my schoolwork, I get to play a quick game. Usually, it is *Where in The World is Carmen Sandiego*? This game is actually about geography, but because it is so much fun, you do not realise it is educational.

All in all, Temple Street Hospital is the best hospital I have ever been in. I would even love to work there when I am old enough. Thank you to everyone who works there.

Friendly fellows in the Ark Cultural Trust garden at Temple Street.

FUNDRAISING

FRIENDS,
FOLLOWERS, SUPPORTERS

FUNDRAISING DEPARTMENT

FRIENDS OF TEMPLE STREET

Ever since the foundation of the Hospital in 1872, the people of Dublin and beyond have given generously of their time and money to The Children's Hospital. In the mid-twentieth century, the great advances in medical science and burgeoning hospital catchment area meant that hospitals struggled to cope with budgets that ran short of the healthcare envisioned for its patients.

Consequently, in the 1960s, the wives and friends of the consultants at Temple Street set up the Friends of The Children's Hospital. The aim of this group was to fund-raise for specific purposes, which would bring the most benefit to the children in the Hospital.

Over the years the committee of the Friends has evolved and regrouped, and in 1996 the present committee of the Friends of The Children's Hospital was formed. In the intervening years they have hosted five Annual Balls, raising over £450,000, in addition to holding musical evenings, film premieres and bridge mornings.

The Friends joined in the main Hospital's fundraising efforts to purchase the MRI scanner, but other projects included funding research into the incidents of cleft lip palate, meningitis and the causes of suicide in young people.

MRI SCANNER

In September 1995 a decision was taken by the Medical Board, Executive Committee and Board of Management to initiate a major fund drive to provide MRI facilities at the Hospital because of the very poor MRI service available to children in Dublin and throughout the country. The target at that time was 1.2 million pounds to cover the cost of the magnet, the anaesthetic equipment and the building costs.

The initiative to build the state-of-the-art facility was completed by the end of 2000. This was achieved with the help of individual donations and fundraising events organised by individuals and groups of children and adults throughout the country, which was much appreciated by the Hospital. The largest event was organised by the ESB, involving a colossal donation from their staff and management. Other major events included the Totts Ball and the fundraising walk to Capetown, South Africa in 2000.

The MRI Unit was officially opened by An Taoiseach, Mr Bertie Ahern on 2 July 2001 at a function in the Hospital, attended by the many hundreds of people who contributed to the 1.3 million pounds required to build and install it.

Until its installation, facilities in Ireland only allowed the most urgent scans to be performed on children. Thankfully, now access is much more readily available and urgent scans are performed as soon as is necessary. There have already been a number of instances where the performance of an early MRI scan allowed a prompt diagnosis and prevented serious long-term consequences. In addition, for the first time, newborn infants with many common neurological complaints in the first few days of life can be examined.

To date this MRI scanner is the only one in the country dedicated to children. All children examined benefit from the fact that their examination is performed in a child-friendly environment with specialist-trained doctors, radiographers and nurses. Sick patients in hospital do not require to be transferred out of the Hospital for examination and this is less stressful for the children and their patients.

Overall, the purchase of the MRI scanner has been a very important and beneficial addition to the patients of the Hospital and others throughout the country.

 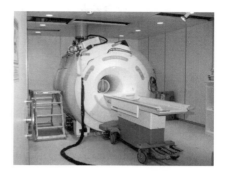

An Taoiseach, Bertie Ahern with Valerie Grimes, radiology services manager, at the opening of the MRI Unit in 2001, with MRI scanner (right).

Gardaí from Fitzgibbon Street at a fundraising presentation in The Children's Hospital, July 2000. Left to right; Area Supt Naoise Rice, Dr Veronica Donoghue, Mr Paul Cunniffe, CEO, Supt Noel McLoughlin, and Mr Fionn MacCumhaill, Board of Management.

GOODWILL AND GRATITUDE

The Children's Hospital owes a great debt of gratitude to the numerous individuals, including politicians and companies, who have contributed their time, money and possessions to events organised over the years for the benefit of the Hospital.

We wish to record the continuing support of groups, such as Belvedere College students, the Motorcyclists' Action Group, St Raphael's Credit Union and the Friends of the Children's Hospital. We thank especially, the present fundraising company and all those people who continue to help us today in their actions and goodwill.

MEMORIES OF A BLOCK-PULLER

Jonathan MacCumhaill

The block-pull every year in aid of Temple Street and the Irish Guide Dogs for the Blind was one of the highlights of my last three years at Belvedere College. There was always great activity in the build-up and preparation for the weeklong walk from Dublin to Galway dragging a block with us along the way. A number of us would persuade our fathers to buy wood, paint and other materials to make the blocks. The making of the blocks was enormous fun and they would eventually take the shape of giant mythological creatures.

Getting these blocks out of the schoolyard wasn't easy! In my first year, even though we had plenty of able mathematicians, no one had thought to measure the height of the school gate! We had to carefully tilt the beast on its side and wheel it out backwards! There was always a danger of crashing, especially if some of the boys lost concentration when the Temple Street nurses would come to help.

So then it was out of the schoolyard, ask our parents for money one last time, and then off we would go. One year we started off in the wrong direction, completing fifteen miles before I had to get everyone to turn back. We then had to walk twice as fast to make up the lost ground, but we made it on time in the end.

I enjoyed the block-pull because the support of the Hospital staff was wonderful. It certainly made a man of me. It's not easy as a young man walking, waving collection boxes and dragging along a large jolly giant, all the way from Dublin to Galway, but it was certainly very rewarding – in every way. In my final year, we raised over £60,000.

2002 Block-pull from Dublin to Galway by students of Belvedere College in aid of Temple Street and the Irish Guide Dogs for the Blind. Inset: Jonathan MacCumhaill.

ESB senior staff with Dr Veronica Donoghue at the opening of the MRI Unit in June 2001.

[**169**]

ENERGY DRIVE

FUNDRAISING DEPARTMENT

The ESB and its staff have had a long and distinguished association with The Children's Hospital, Temple Street going back to 1986 when their first fundraising event occurred. The Hospital at that time needed a nuclear gamma scanner and camera. So on 21 June 1986 the Pole of Light Run began outside the Hospital and over the following ten days, 2,200 ESB runners participated in the 100-mile per day run around the country pushing a pole mounted on a four-wheel chassis eventually reaching 1,000 miles. The Pole Run raised £155,000 for the gamma camera, which is still in use today.

Much later in 1999, the ESB Staff Temple Street Millennium Initiative was formed and turned out to be a unique fundraising partnership with the Friends of The Children's Hospital to raise funds for an MRI scanner. This MRI scanner was needed to enhance the broad range of services on offer in the Hospital and would be the first of its kind in a children's hospital in Ireland.

The ESB and its staff tackled this fundraiser with its usual flair and gusto by asking staff to donate the last two hours of their salary in 1999 – in other words the last two hours of the century to the Hospital. ESB pensioners were asked to contribute one hour but in actual fact donated more. The Board of the company agreed to match pound for pound whatever the staff raised.

This project concluded in March 2001 when ESB chief executive, Ken O'Hara, handed over a cheque for £373,000. However, when the MRI Unit was officially opened on 2 July, Ken returned to do us the honour of turning on the electricity!

6

THE FUTURE

EXCITING TIMES AHEAD

PROF NIALL O'BRIEN

The news that the Hospital is to move to a purpose-built institution on the Mater Hospital grounds offers a great challenge and will no doubt be of tremendous benefit to the children of Dublin, especially the North City but also children from rural areas needing specialist care.

It is with sadness that the Sisters of Charity have relinquished authority over the hospital to the Sisters of Mercy. But one must pay tribute to those Sisters who contributed so much to the welfare of children since 1876. Allied to their work alleviating disease in children, they also developed a Department of Nursing, which to this day is unsurpassable. The standard of nursing care at The Children's Hospital is unique and augmented by much kindness and good humour.

I had the privilege to be a member of the medical staff for thirty years during which time there were many ups and downs, but I am glad to say that the Hospital is stronger than ever and will continue to develop in the new premises.

The Sisters of Mercy are taking on a very viable and exciting institution that will further enhance the future development of the Mater Complex and advance the cause of medicine in Dublin and throughout the country.

Prof Niall O'Brien was Consultant Neonatalogist at The Children's Hospital and retired in 1999.

A CENTRE OF EXCELLENCE
IN THE MAKING

ANTOINETTE WALKER

Like all good ideas, it must have come from somewhere. Was it a quiet word spoken in someone's ear, an earth-shattering eureka or the slow realisation that the winds of change were blowing for the hospital, nestled at the top of Temple Street, looking down over a much-beloved city? And the idea? A new children's hospital co-existing beside a major adult hospital. The first in Ireland.

Indeed the decision came after slow and gradual steps like those of all great changes in consonance with nature. Indeed with earlier building plans revoked, it followed with a certain air of inevitability too. In an age of high-tech medicine, the hospital with its Georgian remnants, endearing nooks and crannies – the old truncated with the new – was feeling the confines of space and time.

Though the question of building a new children's hospital was settled in the late 1990s, the question of guardianship came later. Ultimately, geography was the deciding factor in discussions between two religious congregations on how their ethos to provide the best possible healthcare for the people of Dublin could be realised. And so in 2001 a direct exchange of trusteeships took place – Temple Street (adjacent to the Mater Hospital) was to be governed by the Sisters of Mercy and St Michael's Hospital, Dun Laoghaire by the Sisters of Charity.

Aerial view of the Mater Campus, the site of the new children's hospital.

MATER AND CHILDREN'S HOSPITAL DEVELOPMENT LTD

Building a brand new children's hospital in an age where the mantra of 'cost-effective healthcare' is feverishly chanted is, of course, never going to be easy. In 1999, the Mater and Children's Hospital Development Ltd (MCHD) was established to oversee the new development on the Mater Campus at Eccles Street, and to provide state-of-the-art facilities at the existing Mater Hospital and the new purpose-built Children's University Hospital. Finding funds and expertise, with the huge amount of resources required, inevitably called for extensive planning and consultation. Even for the humble origins of the Children's Hospital on Buckingham Street in 1872, the question of funding was a constant concern, its founders relying on the good graces and bequests of the charitable men and women of Dublin. However, nowadays in a time of proven patient-care systems, patient charters and integrated hospital design against a backdrop of global healthcare, it falls to the State to bear the burden of the cost.

Therefore, putting Celtic Tiger largesse to good use, the Taoiseach, Bertie Ahern announced in November 1999 that the Government would fund the development of the Mater and Children's Hospital at Eccles Street as part of the National Development Plan. In keeping with standards and practices at the Eastern Regional Health Authority and Department of Health and Children, the rigorous set of approval stages for the development project was then set in motion.

- Stage 1 – design brief & cost limit
- Stage 2 – development control plan & cost
- Stage 3 – scheme design & cost plan (subject to planning permission)
- Stage 4 – detail design, production information and tender documentation
- Stage 5 – tender and contract
- Stage 6 – construction
- Stage 7 – commissioning
- Stage 8 – evaluation & feedback

Stages 1 and 2 have been completed thus far, while Stage 3 is shortly to be approved. Stage 1 and 2 put the cost of providing major new acute children's and adult facilities at the Mater Campus at approximately £195 million (at 2001 prices). The completion of Stage 2 saw the Development Control Plan approved by Mr Micheál Martin, Minister for Health and Children, in December 2001. This document, on display in the drop-in information centre at MCHD offices for all to see, established the policy and planning framework for all future developments on the Mater Campus. With a catchment area that stretches north of the River Liffey to Balbriggan, west to Palmerstown, northwest to Blanchardstown, Ashbourne, Garristown and Naul, east to Howth and northeast to Portmarnock, Malahide and Skerries, the scale of the new development is substantial, as one would expect. It is anticipated that by 2004/5 the main development will begin on site and will be completed in 2008/9. So in terms of The Children's Hospital, what then is likely to happen in the meantime?

MEETING NEEDS OF PATIENT, STAFF AND VISITOR

In designing a children's hospital, input from those at the coalface of healthcare is crucial for the design team. Consequently, user groups, such as consultants, nurse managers, departmental managers, line managers and other interested parties were set up as part of Stage 3. Their function is to provide expert knowledge on services and facilities and so formulate and agree on the planning of each department. Moreover, they review existing equipment and plan required equipment schedules. Mindful that departments do not always operate independently of each other but are often interrelated, such as A&E and Radiology, adjacent user groups were also established. Nowadays in modern hospital design teams, one of the key players is the nurse planner, who channels the advice and expert knowledge of the user groups to a design team of architects, planners, surveyors and engineers, etc.

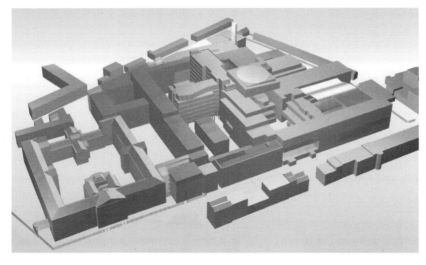

A 3-D view of the long-term plan for the Mater & Children's Hospitals Campus.

NEW SERVICES

In addition to extending existing services and facilities, there are exciting advances too. The hospital's current bed capacity of 135 will be extended to 170. There will be seven operating theatres. There will be provision for a helipad located adjacent to the A&E entrance. Given that Temple Street is currently the country's busiest paediatric A&E Department, and the national centre for neurological, ophthalmic, craniofacial, renal, airways and ENT disorders in children, and more specifically in the case of trauma and neonatal retrieval, the helipad is clearly a priority and timely.

The new children's hospital will provide inpatient psychiatric care, a service previously available only on an outpatient basis at Temple Street. And considering the major advances in neonatology at the hospital in recent years, provision is being made for a fully equipped neonatal ICU. Additionally, intensive care and high dependency units will be upgraded. School facilities, which for so many years were part and parcel of Temple Street, will also be extended. For the proposed layout of wards and departments see Table 1 (*overleaf*).

ENVIRONMENT

In line with modern planning practices and given the scale, nature, location and proposed schedule of the new development, an environmental impact statement (EIS) is being carried out. The type of studies likely to form the basis of the EIS will include; the effects on humans; flora and fauna; soils and water; air, noise and climate; shadow studies; landscape; landscape visualisations; material assets; roads, traffic and transportation; waste; archaeological heritage; and architectural heritage.

Certainly in recent years, many studies have been conducted on the psychological effects of children in hospital and measures to curb any potential ill effects. Design innovation has also meant that nowadays we are seeing patient-focussed hospitals, with a move away from hospital rooms that are excessively clinical, starkly lit, cramped and windowless. Indeed it has been shown that good design has a positive impact on health. By being 'spiritually uplifting', some suggest that hospitals have a curative effect on the sick.

Table 1. Proposed layout of wards and departments at the new children's hospital.

Level O	Level 1	Level 2	Level 3
A&E Outpatients Dept: Neurology Ophthamology Metabolic Ear Nose & Throat Social Work	General Outpatients, including: Dressing Clinic Phlebotomy Orthopaedic General Surgery Dermatology Medical (including Respiratory Medicine) Speech Therapy Dentistry Private Clinic Front Hall Reception (including Coffee Shop & Development Office) Patient and Family Information Centre Admissions and Discharge Lounge	Radiology Physiotherapy Occupational Therapy Seminar Facilities Nursing Administration	Operating Theatres × 7 ICU/HDU (20- bedded unit) Day Ward

Level 4	Level 5	Level 6	
Neonatal ICU Formula Preparation Dietetic Dept Parent Accom. Wards × 2 (one with Dialysis beds)	Inpatient Wards × 3 Day Wards × 5 Inpatient Psychiatry Metabolic	On-call Facilities St Frances & St Clare's Clinics	

Indeed the new hospital is likely to be a veritable healing oasis, given the care and consideration gone into its planning and design. MCHD is committed to creating a 'pleasant and supportive environment' for the children who are patients, for their families and other visitors, and for the staff who will work there.

Moreover, the design values will be very high, expressed in exciting architecture that is also sensitive to the Georgian context of Eccles Street. The circulation routes and layout of departments are designed to facilitate efficient and high-quality medical care, but also to maximise natural light and ventilation. The entrance concourse, a generous double-height space, gives onto a wonderful courtyard, which will be the focus for the hospital as a community. It contains the lifts and corridors so that the movement of the hospital is made visible, a terrace café, a church and contemplation space, and additional spaces for social and recreational use. Here and throughout the hospital there will be green plants, blue sky and fresh breezes to connect everyone with nature and the outside world. The designated specialist play areas will be augmented by playrooms on each of the wards and in certain areas small, planted courtyards to bring further comfort and distraction. The developing tradition of arts practice in the hospital, initiated by a partnership with The Ark Children's Cultural Centre, will also find expression throughout the new hospital.

ENERGY EFFICIENCY

The approach to energy efficiency at the new development is certainly appropriate to the times we live in. A grant was awarded to MCHD by the Irish Energy Centre with view to incorporating potential energy efficiencies at the new hospital through good design. This should ensure that the likely requirements in energy use and output are well conserved. In recent times, the Irish Energy Centre has encouraged the use of renewable energy measures such as passive solar design, passive cooling and ventilation, heat pumps and solar panels in public buildings.

TRAFFIC AND TRAVEL

In the twenty-first century perhaps one of the biggest drawbacks to working in a city hospital is the question of traffic and travel. However, at the new Campus there will be provision for car park spaces, including on call and onsite parking for both hospitals as currently envisaged. Parking will be provided at basement level under the main area of the new buildings. To help the planners, a recent survey of staff travel habits was carried out and its findings will certainly help to address their needs at the new development. Interestingly, 61 per cent of Temple Street staff travel by car to the hospital every day, where 79 per cent were the sole occupants of their cars. Fifty-four per cent of staff live within a six-mile radius of the hospital, and 9 per cent live in the Dublin 9 area.

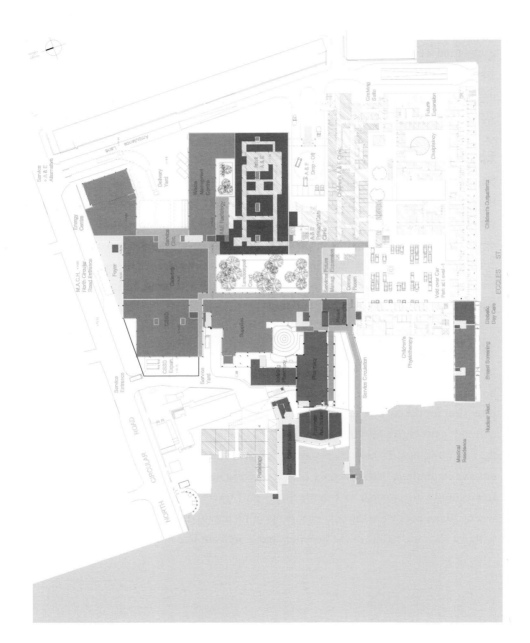

Proposed plan of wards and departments at the new children's hospital.

Various traffic-reduction measures, such as the Luas 3 light-rail system running from Dundrum to Dublin Airport via Drumcondra, Whitehall and Ballymum should facilitate many hospital staff, with proposed spurs and crossings with other Luas lines at Broadstone, Dorset Street and North Circular Road. In addition, a Metro line is proposed from Swords to the City Centre via the airport and Broadstone, terminating at Shanganagh, near Bray. A circular Metro line will connect Blanchardstown, Clondalkin and Tallaght with the City Centre and Broadstone, approximately ten minutes from the Mater Campus. In an effort to assess the volume and type of traffic likely to arrive at the A&E entrances, a travel survey of visitors and patients was conducted in July 2002. Its results will also help planners in the traffic impact assessment.

All in all, no stone has been left unturned in ensuring that the most thorough planning and consultation has taken place, so that the new hospital will be something of which all patients, staff and visitors can be proud. More information on the new developments can be accessed at *www.mchd.ie*.

FUTURE OF OLD HOSPITAL

As guardians of the household for nearly 130 years, the Sisters of Charity left a wonderful legacy and the decision to hand over the trusteeship inevitably came with much sadness and nostalgia. The future of the hospital buildings at Temple Street is yet to be determined, but assuredly will be retained for future medical/community use. However, in saying goodbye to the past and facing a new future, albeit an exciting one, brings uncertainty. But times change and we change with them. And like a parent at the wedding of a cherished child, now grown to maturity, the time has arrived to let go, knowing the union to take place will ensure a future of greater stability and blessing while continuing to be one of Dublin's most beloved institutions.

FINIS CORONAT OPUS

Antoinette Walker is an editor at Blackwater Press. She was seconded to The Children's Hospital in the late 1980s while training as an RGN at St Vincent's Hospital, Elm Park.

A 21st-Century Children's Hospital

Paul Cunniffe

The 130-year history of the recently renamed Children's University Hospital, Temple Street spans three centuries, a period of unprecedented development in scientific, social and political spheres. In 1872, there were still parts of the world to be explored but now man has set foot on the moon and is sending unmanned probes to the outermost planets of our solar system. The Great Famine of 1845–48 had happened just thirty-five years previously, a period within the memory and lifetime of many people living at the time. Ireland was still part of an empire upon which it was said the sun never set – now it's an independent republic.

On a more down-to-earth level, diseases that were once rampant have been conquered and the boundaries of medical knowledge expanded to a degree that would have been incomprehensible to the first medical staff of this hospital. With regard to medical advances, the rate of progress that we have seen over the period of this hospital's history shows no sign of abating. Medical science continues to push out the boundaries of knowledge and new treatments and drugs continue to be produced.

Within our country and society, events such as the so-called 'Celtic Tiger' have drawn migrants from many parts of the world, including Africa, Eastern Europe and Asia. Some of them have come to work in our hospital, but many others come to us because their children need our care. We are becoming a multicultural society and who would have foretold this even ten years ago?

So what of the future and particularly what does it mean for our hospital? Within the first decade of the 21st century, we will have moved into a new purpose-built hospital leaving behind – I am sure with some sadness but also eagerness – our old buildings, some of which have stood for over two hundred years. Located on the campus of the Mater Misericordiae Hospital on Eccles Street, not only will it be a new hospital, but for this country the first full children's hospital that stands alongside a major adult tertiary referral hospital. We will be pioneering in Ireland a model that exists in many parts of the world and which will open up new opportunities for us to develop and prosper. This will also challenge us and test our abilities to adapt and to embrace the possibilities opened to us by change.

However, to look back at the past, even within our own recent memory, should tell us of the difficulties of foretelling the future. All that one can say is that under the trusteeship of the Sisters of Mercy, the Children's University Hospital, Temple Street has a central role in the delivery of acute paediatric hospital care and that the developments in hand will strengthen and enhance their role. We should look forward to the future with confidence and with the reassurance that we have the staff and the skills, and in a few more years, we will have the hospital that we have long desired and aspired to work in.

Mr Paul Cunniffe is Chief Executive at The Children's Hospital.

MISSION STATEMENT

By caring for the sick we participate in the healing ministry of Christ. We honour the spirit of Catherine McAuley and the Sisters of Mercy. We pledge ourselves to respect the dignity of human life; to care for the sick with compassion and professionalism; to promote excellence and equity, quality and accountability.

In our friendly and caring environment, we strive to promote the highest quality of care for all with dignity, compassion and respect. We value our staff and encourage their development.